baby sleep solutions

Finding your own way to easy evenings and peaceful nights

 netmums

parents and experts share advice and experience

with Hollie Smith

headline

First published in 2010 by
HEADLINE PUBLISHING GROUP

1

The purpose of this book is to present solutions that have worked for other parents.
Readers will need to make their own choices, as they know their baby and their
environment best, but must also bear in mind guidelines from the government and
other advisory organisations (including the FSID, see page 179 for details). The author
and publisher cannot take responsibility for any person acting as a result of the
information contained in this book.

Cataloguing in Publication Data is available from the British Library

Trade paperback ISBN 978 0 7553 6101 4

Typeset in Clearface Regular by Palimpsest Book Production Limited,
Falkirk, Stirlingshire

Printed and bound in Great Britain by
Clays Ltd, St Ives plc

HEADLINE PUBLISHING GROUP
An Hachette UK Company
338 Euston Road
London NW1 3BH

www.headline.co.uk
www.hachette.co.uk

Contents

Introduction

Do you remember when you first announced your pregnancy and everyone joked about sleepless nights? And you joined in, knowing that disturbed nights were something that happened to all new mums and dads, but secretly thinking, 'How bad can it really be?' The answer – as those of us with babies who didn't sleep found out – is actually, it can be pretty bad.

Sleep really is one of the things that you take for granted until you aren't getting enough, when it becomes all encompassing. Life starts being marked not into days of the week, but by a never ending series of 'good nights' and 'bad nights'. Each day, you obsessively chart the number of hours' sleep your baby allowed you to have the night before. After a while you start counting the minutes too. You look for patterns, clues and signs about what went right or wrong each night, and try to replicate the patterns that made the 'good nights'. Only to find that each conclusion is disproved by an opposite effect the next time you try it. It's too hot – or is it too cold? It's too noisy – or is it too quiet? Not enough activity the day before – or too much stimulation? Too many daytimes naps – or too few?

The advice you get from family, friends, books and websites often confuses you even more. For every piece of advice suggesting you leave your baby to cry, there is another one that says this may damage her psychologically. A friend advises you to bring him into your bed, while your mother-in-law warns against it. Your mum suggests top-up feeds while your health visitor says this will affect your milk supply.

And why, oh why, does everyone else's baby seem to sleep more than yours? What are you doing wrong? The thoughts and ideas and plans go round and round in your head until you are completely confused, even more exhausted and totally despairing of ever having a proper night's sleep, or even a proper life, again.

I am delighted to be able to offer you this book written by Netmums author Hollie Smith and her expert team and, with it, hope and reassurance that you can and will get your life (and your nights) back. If you've picked up this book before actual problems have set in – perhaps your baby is still tiny, or maybe she hasn't even been born yet – you've done yourself a big favour and you'll reap the rewards later. Don't despair, though, if you need to address an issue that already exists. It's never too late to tackle a sleeping problem.

The main aim of *Baby Sleep Solutions* is helping you to help your baby to sleep well. Broadly speaking, the advice you'll find here offers two different sorts of solutions: those that pre-empt and prevent settling and sleeping problems by setting up good habits in the first place; and those that tackle them once they've arisen. As with all the other Netmums books, *Baby Sleep Solutions* is not intent on prescribing a one-size-suits-all approach and acknowledges that different parents have different outlooks and different lifestyles. It aims to boil down the basics of baby sleep advice (of which there is, let's face it, a mountain out there), and allow you to decide for yourselves what's going to be workable for you and your family. This combination of expert advice and mum-to-mum experience will help you find a solution that is right for you, your baby and your family and, perhaps more importantly, the confidence to carry it out.

Sweet dreams.

Siobhan Freegard,
Founder, Netmums

Meet the team

Hollie Smith

Hollie is a journalist and parenting author who has written six books, including two other titles for Netmums, *Toddling to Ten*, and *Baby's First Year*. A member of Netmums for the past eight years, she is a firm believer in the importance of friendship, support and solidarity among mums. Hollie lives in Bedfordshire with her husband and two daughters, aged eight and five.

Louise Cremonesini

Louise qualified as a nurse in 1993 and spent five years working in adult intensive care before training as a specialist children's nurse and working for ten years in paediatric intensive care at Great Ormond Street and the Royal Brompton hospitals. She then undertook a BA (hons) degree in Public Health and started a career as a health visitor for Ealing Primary Care Trust, for whom she spent three years running sleep clinics. Louise is currently studying for an Msc in Child Protection and is a health visitor in a Sure Start Children's Centre in the West Midlands. She is married to David and they have a three-year-old daughter.

Dr David Cremonesini

David studied medicine at Oxford University and St George's Hospital Medical School in London, and has been working in paediatrics since 1997. He spent two years at the John Radcliffe Hospital in Oxford where he developed an interest in respiratory paediatrics and allergy. He is now a general paediatric and neonates consultant at a hospital in the West Midlands.

Maggie Fisher

Maggie qualified as a nurse in 1977 at The London Hospital, where she also completed a course on specialist and intensive care for the newborn, and worked in the neonatal intensive care unit. She has worked as a health visitor for 27 years in London and Hampshire, and ran a sleep support group for 15 years. She has a postgraduate diploma in Promoting the Mental Health of Infants and Children and has contributed to a book about parenting in public health. Maggie is currently chair of Unite/CPHVA (Community Practitioners' and Health Visitors' Association) Health Visitors' Forum and works for Netmums as a health visitor parent supporter. She lives in Hampshire and is married with three children, a 15-year-old daughter and sons aged 20 and 23.

1 Setting up for good sleep

Why is sleep such a big deal, anyway?

We all need a certain amount of sleep to survive – that's a fact. A lack of sleep leaves us short of energy, enthusiasm and concentration: qualities you really need when you're trying to cope with modern family life. And, more seriously, lack of sleep can trigger, or contribute to, really big problems like depression, relationship difficulties and anger issues. So sleeping well is vital for your physical and mental health. Sleep well and you'll wake up refreshed and more able to cope with whatever life – and parenting – has to throw at you.

Sleeping well is vital to your baby's well-being, too. Infants and children require even more sleep than adults and, like us, they'll become exhausted and miserable if they don't get enough. And sleeping well is particularly crucial during childhood, as it is during sleep that much of their growth and development takes place.

What the netmums say

Sleep *is* a big deal!

When you're sleep-deprived for months at a time you can end up feeling tired, sick and miserable, and it makes everything about parenting much harder. My three children have all been rubbish sleepers and I remember so many times in their first few years thinking that everything would be so much easier if I wasn't so tired all the time. When you're getting enough sleep and you're well rested you have more energy, which can make all the difference when coping with the challenges of parenting. And it means you can enjoy your children much more, too.

Kathy from Bromley, mum to Elizabeth, six, Daniel, four, and Rachel, one

Sleep is so, so, so important. My first daughter didn't sleep through the night until she was four months old – not bad going, you may say, but I think if it had gone on longer I would have ended up suffering from depression. When I eventually got her to sleep, *I* couldn't sleep. My second daughter slept through from six weeks, and what a blessing that was. I'm more like my normal self again and I have the energy and motivation to have fun and enjoy my children. Sleep makes the world go round, although I admit I'm probably obsessed with getting it. A lie-in would be nice now, but hey, I'm not going to push it.

Eleanor from Dagenham, mum to Ruby, two, and Daisy, six months

In my opinion sleep – or lack of it – is the hardest issue we've had to face as parents, apart from illness. My son has always been a terrible sleeper. However, for the first six months or so it didn't really bother us. Being first timers, we were excited by it all and thought we would soon be putting him down to 'sleep through'. A year or so later, he is still waking every night, two or three times on a really good day but mostly every hour or so. I can safely say it's putting a huge strain on both me and my hubby individually and as a couple. I love my little boy more than anything but I can't help thinking we've been dealt a rough deal when I compare younger babies to him, then I feel guilty for being so bothered, as at least he's healthy and that's the main thing. Sleep problems make you question your ability as a parent and that can be so destructive.

Charlotte from Leicester, mum to Logan, one

In my opinion sleep is a *massive* deal. It's the main subject at most parent and baby groups and online, in baby forums and coffeehouse chats – and of most conversations I have with my mother-in-law and mum! From day one, grandparents on both sides were commenting, 'I can't believe she doesn't sleep. You/her daddy slept through from two weeks', which at the time, when you're a new mum and not completely sure you know what you're doing, makes you feel pretty rubbish. And it doesn't end when they're babies. I was in the supermarket queue the other day when I got asked by the lady behind me, 'Does she sleep?' It's madness!

Nova from Manchester, mum to Poppy, three

Planning ahead

If your baby is very new, or yet to make an appearance, take advantage of the head start by reading up on baby sleep matters, planning your sleeping arrangements and thinking about what your attitude towards your baby's sleep is likely to be. Will you, for instance, be a stickler for routine and rigid sleep schedules? Will you go for a more baby-led lifestyle and opt for bedsharing and random bedtimes? Or will you aim for something in the middle of the two? Your general mindset as parents will be influential, as well as your lifestyles.

Where your baby sleeps is likely to be the main question in your minds when preparing for a new arrival. Lots of parents go to great lengths to prepare a nursery, complete with a brand new cot. But, in fact, official advice is that the safest place to put your baby – for the first six months of her life – is close to your own bedside (there's lots more on safe sleeping in the following chapter) and many parents find a crib or Moses basket (see below), which easily fits in their own room and may be portable, is a better option for the early months.

Perhaps you are actively making plans to bedshare with your baby. Although official guidance tends to warn against bedsharing, some parents choose to do so (while still more end up doing so, even if they didn't plan to) and find it's a sleep solution that suits them. You don't have to feel guilty about planning to bedshare, as long as you also plan to take the relevant safety advice on board. (This is outlined in detail on page 27.) If it's something you're determinedly opting for from the start, you'll definitely need to think about your sleeping arrangements and make sure your set-up is as safe as possible.

Wherever your thoughts lie, do remain flexible. By all means research particular theories and buy what you need in the way of nursery furniture and other sleep-related paraphernalia (there are some ideas for kitting yourself out in advance, below, and masses more from specialist suppliers online). But remember that what you *think* will work for you and what *actually* works out for you may turn out to be different things – not least because your baby may have her own ideas! And do involve your partner or co-parent in any planning, because it's an issue that you need to be united on.

Above all, psych yourself up for what will potentially be a very tiring new lifestyle. Few first-time parents are prepared for the upheaval that a new baby brings. The broken nights and lack of sleep are two of the biggest shocks to bear (although, if you suffered from pregnancy insomnia, you may have had a small taste of what's to come). Truth is, if you've just had a baby or you're about to have one, your life – and your sleeping habits – are about to change in a big way.

What the netmums say

Planning your approach . . . flexibly

Before I had my daughter, I decided exactly what I was going to do: she would have a good routine. I didn't read the books, I just knew that was how it was going to work. Oh my God, how wrong was I! After an emergency c-section I was barely able to pick her up, which didn't help with 'the plan'. I now have a baby who doesn't sleep much, feeds lots and has reflux. So she gets fed to sleep every night and we just go with the flow through the day. We've established our own routine, which is fairly flexible. Thankfully she's the happiest, smiliest baby I've ever known.
Rebecca from Penrith, mum to Katie, three months

I planned to have babies who would go to sleep in their own beds, would not need rocking to sleep and could settle down on their own. But, in the end, it wasn't so easy. My first child had separation issues from an early age and she was just over a year old by the time she was finally able to settle herself at night. With my second, things were even worse as she suffered from reflux and was also very clingy – she could only take small amounts of milk and never slept for more than two to three hours at a time. I hadn't even heard of co-sleeping then but, in retrospect, I wish we'd tried it as I'm sure we would both have got more sleep as I could have settled her more easily, and maybe I would have been able to breastfeed her for longer. She was still waking up several times a night at two, and she was three before she slept through consistently.

Donna from Manchester, mum to Caitlin, six, and Lucy, five

I read loads of books while pregnant and decided to take a little bit from them all and do it my way. I used to write everything I did down and for us it worked brilliantly. By the time he was a month old, I didn't need to keep writing it down, as it was all second nature. I used to joke he was my little clock.

Deborah from Bexley, mum to Thomas, one

With my first, I had set ideas about our son sleeping in his own cot each night – cue baby arriving and feeding every hour and me so shattered we ended up co-sleeping for the first year! Determined not to make the same mistakes again, we've put our daughter in her cot every night and she hasn't co-slept at all, and has been much better at self-settling.

Jenna from Wolverhampton, mum to Jude, two, and Arabella, eight months

What your baby needs for sleeping

Moses baskets

These are lightweight, portable and much more compact than a full-size cot – depending on how big, or long, your baby is and when she starts to roll over, they can usually be used for somewhere between three and six months (some very big babies outgrow them in a matter of weeks). You can buy a stand separately, which allows you to keep your baby off the floor and away from draughts. You can also buy a 'rocking' version of these stands but, as with cribs (see below), if you set a precedent of rocking your baby to sleep, you may find you have to keep it up beyond the point where you're happy to.

Moses baskets seem to provide a cosier and more secure environment than cots, making them more suitable for newborns who are still trying to acclimatise to life outside the womb. More usefully still, they're small enough to fit by your bedside so you can have your baby in your room at night. And they're portable, which is a boon in the early weeks when your baby naps a lot during the day and you want her near you while you're downstairs, too. The disadvantage is that they're costly for something you don't get a lot of use from, which is why most people borrow or buy them second-hand. Don't forget:

- To always take extreme care when lifting or carrying your baby in a Moses basket – in fact, safety campaigners say it is best to avoid doing so altogether. Instead, you should take your baby out and put her somewhere safe while you carry the basket to where you need it.
- To double-check the Moses basket stand locks firmly and provides a steady base. And be sure to buy a new mattress, which fits snugly to the sides of the basket, if you're borrowing or buying second-hand.
- That when the time comes to make the transition to a full-size cot, it can help to put your baby's Moses basket in the cot for a few nights, allowing her to get used to the new environment first.

Cribs

A pricier but sturdier and slightly more long-term solution than a Moses basket, cribs are usually useful for up to six months (again, it will depend on your baby's size and how mobile she is: safety campaigners warn that they're not suitable once your baby is able to sit up, kneel, or get on all fours) and might be a good compromise if you don't have room for a full-size cot in your bedroom. They look nice but don't tend to be easily portable, one of the main advantages of the Moses basket. Most have an optional swinging or sliding mechanism, which you may want to use with caution: as with the rocking version of the Moses basket stand, if your baby comes to rely on being rocked to sleep, you're setting up a habit that you may have to keep up long after you'd like to stop (there's more on 'sleep associations' on page 71).

Cots and cot-beds

You don't *have* to have a Moses basket or a crib: some babies happily settle straight away in a full-size cot. There's a huge market for cots and they come in many styles and varying sizes – the space you have available is probably your main consideration. Two useful features to look for are an adjustable base, which means you can alter the height of the cot (as your baby grows, for safety's sake, you will need to lower it so she can't climb out), and drop-sides, which make getting your baby in and out easier. Cot-beds often make good economic sense, as they convert into a bed that your little one can use well beyond the toddling years. (On the other hand, if you settle for a cot-bed and then have another baby, you'll have to buy a new cot, anyway.) If you're buying a cot second-hand or have been given one, don't forget to:

- Make sure it's at least 49.5cm (20") deep and that the bars are vertical, with 4.5cm to 6.5cm (2" to 3") spacing in between them.

- Buy a new mattress and make sure it fits properly – there should not be a gap of more than 4cm (2") anywhere between the edge of the mattress and the bars of the cot.
- Strip and re-paint it, if there are signs of peeling paint or splinters. Remove layers of paint from very old cots with care, as it could contain harmful traces of lead: modern paints are lead-free, and therefore safe, but for extra peace of mind, eco-friendly paints specially designed for nurseries are available from specialist paint suppliers and large DIY stores.

Baby hammocks

According to manufacturers, these suspended, nest-like hammocks are suitable from birth to 12 months and promise to provide: comfort; gentle movement; and a 'womb-like' environment, which will make for a good night's sleep. They are pricey though, which is possibly why there doesn't, as yet, seem to be a big market for them.

Bedside cribs/cots

Also called 'side-car' cots, these offer a compromise if you want to bedshare with your baby but you're concerned about safety or discomfort. They attach firmly to the side of a normal adult bed, allowing you close proximity to your baby without any risks. There are also more ideas for safer ways to bedshare on page 27.

Bedding

Sheets and blankets are a popular option for a newborn as you can add and remove layers easily, according to temperature (for safety reasons this is really important – there's more detail on page 23). Make sure you get the right size of sheet, depending on the kind of bed your baby is sleeping in, and have a good few spares as they may end up being frequently soiled. Lightweight, cellular blankets (the sort with the holes) are ideal as they won't let your baby get too hot – one or two's usually enough, depending on the temperature.

Baby sleeping bags are increasingly popular and many parents swear they aid better sleep as they can't be kicked off, like sheets and blankets, so a little one will never wake up as a result of becoming cold. They're suitable from birth but you do need to make sure you've got the right size, as well as the right tog-rating for the weather (so you'll probably need to have four – one for summer and one for winter, and a spare of each for when you're washing).

Room thermometer

This simple and inexpensive piece of equipment is one of the few absolute necessities, allowing you to see at a glance what the temperature is in your baby's room (see page 23 for more detail). They can be ordered from the Foundation for the Study of Infant Death Syndrome (FSID) website for a few pounds, and often come as a freebie with baby magazines, or when you buy a cot, baby bedding or sleeping bag.

Baby monitors

There are lots of electronic baby monitors on the market (including video monitors that allow you to see as well as hear your sleeping baby) and they are popular with parents – particularly first-timers – because they can give peace of mind once your baby is in bed and you are elsewhere in the house where you cannot hear them, or once your baby is in a room of her own.

However, baby monitors aren't essential – particularly if you have a small home or thin walls and are likely to hear your baby if she wakes or cries, anyway. In fact, lots of parents buy them and find they don't use them much after all, or that they're happy to turn them off once their baby's past a certain age, so they're no longer disturbed by all the fidgeting, snuffling, snorting and other perfectly normal night noises that babies make.

Also available now are movement monitors (sometimes known as apnoea or breathing monitors) which are designed to warn you if your baby stops breathing by sounding a warning alarm if it detects a lack of movement. However, according to FSID there isn't any evidence that these actually prevent cot death and in fact they have a number of drawbacks – not least the fact that they can give off 'false alarms' (for example, when the sensor pad becomes detached or when a baby's breathing movements are so small they cannot be picked up), which are stressful. The Foundation's recommendation is that these sorts of monitors are only used in special cases, for instance, where a baby has a diagnosed sleep disorder, or by parents who have previously suffered a cot death, and should always be used under the careful supervision of a doctor and a health visitor.

Prams, slings and bouncy chairs

Chances are your little one will spend some time napping in her pram or buggy, carrycot, sling, car seat or bouncy chair – so bear that in mind when buying these things and look for optimum comfort. There are some health and safety issues to take into account, though – there's more detail on these in the section on safe napping on page 90.

Curtains and blinds

Putting your baby to bed in a darkened or dimly lit room will help her grasp the idea that evening equals bedtime, so curtains or a well-fitting blind in the room your baby sleeps in will be useful for spring and summer months. Some parents are big fans of blackout blinds, which make the room totally dark, and can be a good way of encouraging your baby to sleep later in the morning. The argument against them is that if your baby becomes too reliant on total darkness in order to drop off, you might struggle to get her to sleep when you're not at home and you could end up having to take blackout blinds with you every time you're out or away – or at least be prepared to rig up some kind of temporary solution with a bit of blackout fabric and drawing pins.

A dim lamp or nightlight

You'll need to see what you're doing at night when you go to change your baby, give her a feed or offer comfort, but it's crucial to keep the lighting very dim when you go about any night-time business (as well as keeping things quiet and low-key – for more on this see page 72). A small, shaded lamp with a very low wattage light bulb, a dimmer switch on the main light, or a nightlight (which she may also make use of when she's older, if a fear of the dark ever kicks in), will be a useful addition to her sleeping environment.

Comforters

A comforter in the form of a dummy, favoured toy, or a piece of blanket or clothing can certainly be a useful aid to settling your baby once she's grown attached to it. There's a strong argument against them, though, which is that if your baby needs something like this to get to sleep at night and she's dropped it out of her cot or cannot easily find it, she's likely to wake you so that you can find it for her. They can also become lost easily, which can be a bit of a disaster if you've only got the one and your baby simply can't settle without it.

Dummies have traditionally got a bad press, but they don't have to be harmful if used sensibly. And in fact, they are now specifically recommended by FSID (see page 24), which says that *routinely* giving your baby a dummy at night, every night, during the first six months of your baby's life, may help reduce the risk of cot death.

(Although, avoid them in the first few weeks if your baby is breast-feeding in case it interferes with her ability to suck at the breast, see page 50.)

Also widely available these days are other commercially produced comfort objects. Although these make nice gifts, it is not really necessary to fork out for one of these, as your baby is just as likely to grow fond of a small square of muslin or cellular blanket. There's more on dummies and comforters on page 50.

Musical toys and mobiles

Like comforters, these can seem helpful at first but, on the other hand can quickly become a 'sleep association' you could do without if your baby won't go to sleep without it and you need to keep returning to wind it up or set it moving!

What the netmums say

What your baby needs for sleeping

We had a Moses basket but ended up only using it downstairs and even that was only for a few weeks – he was a big baby so I put him straight into a cot at night, which worked fine. At first we used sheets and blankets but he was very fidgety and kicked them off, so we tried a sleeping bag and it was fab. We never used monitors, although we bought them.
Zoe from Swindon, mum to Jayden, three

With both girls we used a crib that was in our bedroom until they were five to six months old, then they went into a cotbed in their own room. Someone I knew gave me a loan of a Moses basket, but both my babies were long and I didn't want to waste money buying a mattress for something that would probably only last a few weeks. Cribs are sturdy and they seem to be safer. I bought mine second-hand, so it wasn't too expensive. I'd say borrow if you can, or buy second-hand if you can't afford to buy brand new.

Meg from Belshill, mum to Eve, three, and Louise, four months

We borrowed a Moses basket and bought a rocking stand before Katy was born and put this beside our bed. We do also have a cot stored away for when she gets too big for it, which will just about fit in our bedroom. Bedding-wise we use 'Grobags' [a popular brand of baby sleeping bag] and have done since Katy was born. I find them very convenient and it's reassuring to think that there's no way that she can get the bedclothes over her head and that she can't kick them off.

Liz from Godalming, mum to Katy, four months

Our daughter didn't stay in her Moses basket for very long as she preferred our bed and got too big for it at eight weeks. We then moved her to her cot and used half of that mattress for a few more months. We were nervous of overheating her in a sleeping bag at first, as she was a summer baby, but once we started with one we never looked back. We never used a monitor as we have a small flat, but have found blackout blinds are very good in summer – I reckon they give us an extra hour's sleep in the morning, at least.

Dinah from Harrow, mum to Samantha, one

Both my babies have slept at night in a 'side-car' cot – a normal cot with one side removed, which is fixed to my side of the bed so I can feed easily at night. Liam stayed in it until he was three, then moved to a big bed, and Niamh is there now. I also used baby sleeping bags for both, as they are much more convenient for rolling them over to feed at night. *Heather from Canterbury, mum to Liam, three, and Niamh, six months*

2 What new parents need to know about sleep

The science of sleep

Scientists still haven't really got to the bottom of sleep and why we do it. What *is* clear is that we all need sleep to refresh ourselves physically and mentally, in order to function normally the following day. And for babies, children and adolescents sleep is particularly vital for their development and health, because during sleep a release of growth hormones takes place and the immune system is boosted.

We know there are two distinct types of sleep, which we all move through in 'cycles' – light or REM (Rapid Eye Movement) sleep (also sometimes known as dream sleep, since it's during REM sleep that we do all our dreaming) and deep or non-REM sleep. When your baby is in REM sleep, you may notice his limbs jerking and eyelids flickering, and his breathing may be shallow or irregular. In deep sleep, he'll be totally relaxed and still, his breathing will be slow, deep and regular, and he'll be harder to rouse.

Why do babies wake up so much?

There are good reasons to explain why babies don't sleep well. During the first few months of life, about 50 per cent of a newborn's sleep is REM sleep (this decreases gradually until, by around three years, it makes up about a third of sleep and, for older children and adults, it's closer to a quarter). Babies also have shorter sleep cycles than the rest of us, going through a complete cycle around every 50 minutes (as opposed to cycles of about 90 minutes in adulthood). So, it's a scientific fact that babies are more likely to wake during the night than adults.

We all tend to be roused naturally as we move between different phases of sleep. Although you may not realise it, you probably wake several times a night – even assuming you *aren't* being disturbed by your baby. But while adults and older children have learned to roll over and return to the land of nod straight away, young babies are more likely to wake up fully, in need of a feed or comfort to get them back to sleep – which, of course, is where you come in.

So, if you're struggling because your baby is waking you at night, it might help to remind yourself that he's not doing it deliberately. Babies are physiologically incapable of sleeping for very long stretches of time at first, and even once it becomes a physical possibility for them, they will not necessarily settle and sleep through as a matter of instinct – many need help from you to get there.

How much sleep does my baby need?

You'll find many a chart offering the answer to this question. However, there is a lot of variation in what's normal, so there's probably no point in getting hung up on what the charts say. Try looking at it in more general terms, rather than counting up the zzzs: if your baby seems alert, refreshed and happy when he wakes in the morning, and he's napping sufficiently to see him through the rest of the day without becoming miserable, he's getting enough sleep. Meanwhile, though, to give you an idea of what's *average*:

- Newborns sleep 16–20 hours out of every 24 (with very little difference between napping in the day and sleeping at night).
- By three months the required amount is closer to 15 hours out of 24 (with around two-thirds of this sleep occurring at night and a third during nap-times in the day).
- By one year it's 14 out of 24 hours (with an average 11.5 hours taking place at night and 2.5 hours during daytime naps).
- By two, it's 11–12 hours (with almost all of this taking place at night, except for up to an hour of daytime napping).

Some babies just sleep better than others!

Sleep is often the number one topic of conversation at any gathering of mums and babies. And you can bet your bootees that there'll always be at least one other baby whose sleeping habits are a whole lot better than yours. It's worth bearing in mind that not every parent is totally honest about these things. And, anyway, comparing and contrasting is a pointless exercise because all babies are *not* the same. They don't necessarily conform to a single, set pattern of behaviour and, just as with adults, some babies simply require less sleep than other babies, while some have more need for human contact – evenings and night-times being no exception. In fact, very often parents of more than one child will report that even within their own brood – and in spite of doing everything the same – there are 'good' and 'bad' sleepers (although we shouldn't really label our children as such, as the following paragraph explains). Fact is, some babies just sleep better than others.

The psychology of sleep

So, sleep's a big deal. Life's hard when you're not getting enough of it – and it's made even harder sometimes by the pressure on modern parents to be living perfect lives and bringing up perfect children. A baby who sleeps well is deemed a 'good' baby, which implies that parents with babies who sleep well did something clever to achieve it – and makes the less lucky ones feel like failures.

Try not to look at sleep or settling problems as your fault. Even if you know you've set up some less-than-desirable habits (and someone is delightedly informing you about the 'rod for your own back' you made as a result), don't waste energy feeling bad about it. All parents have been there at some point – you do whatever you can to cope with what's on your plate at that point in time. And anyway, bad habits (or let's call them 'unhelpful' habits) can be made good easily enough.

It's also sensible – even if you do suspect you have one – to avoid labelling your little one a 'bad' sleeper, because it's always harder to address a situation you feel negatively about. There's a theory that parents who tend to be anxious or over-attentive are more likely to encourage poor sleep habits than good ones. So – while easier said than done – a chilled-out approach is your best bet.

Whose life is it, anyway?

It's not just babies that are different – parents come in all sorts of varieties, too. You may be the sort of parent who requires peaceful evenings and undisturbed nights, with a baby who's tucked up in his own cot upstairs, while you settle down in the exclusive company of your partner. Or you may be the type who's happy to hold your baby close all evening and attend to him whenever he cries throughout the night. You don't have to feel that whichever way you choose, you are doing it wrong. It's up to you to do what feels right and what works best for you, your partner and your child or children.

There's no quick fix

Unfortunately, there's no quick fix or magic bullet if you're trying to set up good sleep habits, or overturn bad ones. It's best to consider these things gradual processes, with progress best made in small steps. You'll almost certainly have to be realistic . . . and patient, too.

Exactly what *is* a sleep problem, anyway?

There's no single answer to this question. One parent's sleep problem may be very different from another's. And, in any case, a certain level of sleep 'problems' are only to be expected with a very young baby. But, generally speaking, you have a sleep problem if your baby is more than six months old and his refusal to settle in the evening or his waking at night-time (or both) are affecting either him, you, or anyone else in your family, for the worse – physically or mentally.

One thing's for sure, if you believe your baby (and you) is suffering from a sleep problem, you're not alone. Statistics vary but, according to one US report, 76 per cent of parents had 'issues' surrounding their child's sleep that they wished they could change. And a recent UK poll found that the average parent loses a whopping two months of sleep during their baby's first year, with 38 per cent still being woken in the night by their one-year-old.

As a general rule, baby and child sleep problems ease up over the years (it's a cliché but it's true: there'll probably come a time when your 'baby' sleeps so soundly you have to shake him awake for school in the morning). But most parents don't want to wait years – they need a good night's sleep much sooner than that! And, if that's the case, you will probably have to take steps to change the situation yourself. The good news is that, almost invariably, a healthy baby of six months plus *can* be helped to get through the night without disturbing you. There's more on how in chapter five.

Safe sleeping

All parents, whatever their attitude, need to know about the safety issues surrounding babies and sleep. Thankfully, deaths from SIDS (Sudden Infant Death Syndrome, usually referred to as cot death) have fallen by 75 per cent since the early 1990s when an awareness campaign was launched, but, sadly, 300 babies still die every year suddenly and unexpectedly in their sleep for no clear reason.

Experts can't pinpoint a single likely cause for cot death, but they do know there are a number of factors which push up the risk and, hence, there's a long list of guidelines aimed at reducing it. The advice that follows is based on information from the Foundation for the Study of Infant Death Syndrome (FSID).

Reducing the risk of cot death

- Put your baby to sleep in a cot, crib or Moses basket and in the same room as you for the first six months of his life. Studies show that these two factors combined add up to the safest sleep environment for your baby.
- Don't smoke round your baby, or anywhere in the house. Research shows that exposure to smoke – both during pregnancy and after birth – is a very definite risk factor in cot death.
- Always put your baby to sleep on his back. If he begins to roll

over before six months and you notice he's turned over on to his front, move him gently on to his back. However, you don't need to worry about flipping him over once he's older than six months and past the main risk age for cot death.

- Rather than having your baby sleep with his head at the top of his cot, as an adult would, make up your baby's bedding at the foot and have him sleep there. This is sometimes called the 'feet-to-foot' sleeping position because his feet are at the foot of the cot. This way he won't be able to wriggle down under his covers. A baby sleeping bag is a safe alternative to sheets and blankets (and your baby needn't be placed at the foot of the cot), but make sure you've got the right size and the right tog-rating for the temperature.

- Don't let your baby get too hot when he's sleeping. The temperature in his room should be around 16–20 degrees centigrade and he shouldn't be near a radiator or heater. A room thermometer is the best way to keep tabs. Don't overdress your baby – a vest and sleepsuit is fine – and don't give him too much bedding – a single sleeping bag or a sheet and one or two cellular blankets (see page 9) should be plenty, whatever the season.

- Don't let your baby have a pillow or a duvet before he is one year old.

- Make sure your baby's mattress is clean and dry. Buy a new one when kitting out your nursery, and if your cot, crib or basket is second-hand, be sure it fits snugly.

- Never allow yourself to fall asleep with your baby in an armchair or sofa. Research suggests this is a *particularly* risky situation. Sit in an upright chair to feed your baby, so you're less likely to get so comfy you become sleepy. You could also perhaps ask your partner to remain awake with you while you feed to help prevent you dropping off.

- Breastfeed your baby. Studies show that breastfed babies are at lower risk of cot death. However, if you breastfeed your baby in bed at night, don't forget to put him back in his cot after you've fed him – or make certain you are following the bedsharing guidelines, see below.

- Consider giving your baby a dummy at night. Recent research has found that giving your baby a dummy when settling him at night – every night – may help to reduce the risk of cot death, as it's believed the dummy keeps the mouth, and therefore the airways, open. If you're breast-feeding, though, you shouldn't offer a dummy in the first month or so, and it's a good idea to try removing a dummy from six months, when the cot death risk drops dramatically. You don't have to worry about replacing the dummy should it drop out in the night while your baby is asleep. There's more on dummies on page 12.

- Always get advice or medical attention for your baby if he seems poorly and you are concerned – particularly if he is wheezy or having trouble breathing; is being sick; is hot and sweaty; is pale; has a rash; or is not responding to you normally. If you can't get hold of your GP, call NHS Direct. [Numbers are listed in the back of this book.]

Louise says: Cot death risk has been significantly reduced in part due to the message given by health visitors for babies to sleep on their backs. Don't forget your baby also needs lots of 'tummy time', to aid his development and to help prevent plagiocephaly or 'flat-head syndrome'. 'Back to sleep, front to play' is a good motto to follow. Just be sure to stay with your baby when he's on his tummy.

To share, or not to share?

The official advice from the government and the NHS, as well as FSID, is that sleeping in the same bed as your baby is best avoided. This is because, over the years, a number of studies have linked bedsharing to cot death – although it is believed to be a combination of bedsharing with one or more other factors (see below) that is most dangerous. In addition, a small number of *explained* accidental deaths, such as crushing or falling from a bed, occur as a result of bedsharing. But the facts and figures are complex – and it's simpler for the government to issue generalised guidelines to the public, hence the blanket advice not to sleep with your baby.

In reality, lots of parents *do* wind up sleeping with their babies at some point – around half, according to statistics. Many people find it enjoyable and swear it's a better way to get a good night's sleep. And not all the experts believe bedsharing is necessarily a bad idea. Some pro-breastfeeding organisations, for example the National Childbirth Trust and Unicef, point out that it's easier to breastfeed at night if your baby is in bed with you. Others such as Deborah Jackson, Jean Liedloff and Margot Sunderland have written books in which they argue that bedsharing was the norm historically (and still is, in other cultures across the world), and that it's a positive thing for parents and babies, for lots of reasons. (Details of these books are included in the appendix.)

What is certain is that if you *do* bedshare, there are vital safety guidelines to follow. And, safety apart, there are other considerations to think about – so be sure to weigh up the pros and cons first before you try it.

Dr David says: It's an undisputed fact that the *safest* place for a baby in the first six months of life is in a cot, beside the parental bed. My advice to anyone who does have their baby in bed with them would be to follow all the relevant safety guidelines – in particular, never to share if you've been smoking, drinking alcohol, or taking a drug or medication that could make you drowsy. If you're not safe to drive, you're definitely not safe to bedshare.

Advantages of bedsharing

- It's a good way to get close and cuddly with your baby (and for your partner to, too).
- It makes night-time breastfeeding easier as you don't have to get up to feed your baby.
- It's easier to settle your baby if he wakes in the night. (On the other hand, some say he's likely to be stimulated by you being there and therefore *less* likely to settle.)

Disadvantages of bedsharing

- You need to give careful consideration to the safety issues (see below).
- Your baby's wriggling and moving may disturb you (and vice versa); and if your baby is easily roused, you may be tempted to feed more frequently than is actually necessary, which could set up a tiring pattern.
- Your baby is likely to become dependent on you and proximity to you in order to get off to sleep again when he wakes – you may find you have to go to bed with your baby, or keep him up until you go to bed, too, and this could set up a pattern that is hard to break when you want to, further down the line (for example, if you want your bed back, or if

a new baby comes along). And the older your baby is when you try to move him to his own bed, the harder it is likely to be!

- Opportunities for sex or cuddling with your partner are reduced. In fact, some couples find that disagreement on whether to bedshare or not can become a real sticking point – you both need to be happy about the arrangement if you don't want it to become a source of arguments.

What you need to know if you *do* sleep with your baby

Whether you make a determined choice to bedshare or you didn't intend to but find it's something you end up doing anyway, you don't have to feel guilty about it as long as you've done everything you possibly can to reduce the risks. Here's what you need to know.

Tips for safe bedsharing

- Don't bedshare at all if you or your partner are smokers; have been drinking alcohol or taking medication or drugs that make you drowsy; or 'feel very tired'. FSID also says that it's risky to sleep with a baby who was premature, or a low birth weight (under 5½ lbs).
- Never put your baby into an adult bed alone, even if he's too young to roll over, as he could wriggle into danger. This means that if you bedshare, you'll either have to go to bed at the same time as your baby, or put him to bed in the evening in his own cot, crib or Moses basket, and transfer him to your bed later on when you're ready for sleep.
- Consider investing in a bedside or 'side-car' cot for your

baby. There are several on the market now, but you need to be certain they are very securely fixed to the side of your bed. Alternatively, you could look into buying a special 'nest', which is a small portable mattress with sides, designed with safer bedsharing in mind.

- If you and your baby sleep in the same bed make sure it's a large one with plenty of room for everyone – some families find the only way to make enough room is for one adult to move into the spare room for a while. If you and your partner are both in bed, it's probably safest for your baby to sleep in between you. In any case, be wary of putting your baby against a wall where he could fall down the crack – you can avoid this risk by firmly wedging rolled up towels down the gap – or on the outside of the bed, where he could fall on to the floor. It's not a good idea to add any kind of bedrail or makeshift guard against the side of the bed to avoid him falling out as your baby could become trapped against it. Sleeping on a mattress on the floor is one way to avoid both problems.

- Make sure your mattress is firm and that the sheets you are sleeping on are firmly fitted or tucked in. Waterbeds are a definite no-no. The mattress should fit snugly against the head or foot boards.

- Follow the normal safe sleeping guidelines about temperature and position. Always put your baby on his back (remember to roll him over if he's been on his side feeding), make sure your room is the right temperature (16–20 degrees centigrade) and that your baby is not overdressed. Keep your own bedding to a minimum – if you have a duvet and pillows, you need to keep them well away from your baby's head. You can help protect your baby from moving up and down the bed and getting entangled in bedding pillows by sleeping curled around him in a 'c' position.

- Don't allow pets to share the bed. And if you're inviting an older sibling into the mix, don't allow them to sleep right next to your baby.
- Never sleep with your baby on a sofa or armchair. Research shows this is one of the riskiest situations of all. Don't fall asleep with your baby on your chest. He could easily roll off.
- Bear in mind that the risks associated with bedsharing are higher the younger the baby.

What the netmums say

To bedshare . . . or not

I don't really have a view on bedsharing either way. When I was breastfeeding my little one was in bed with me and it suited me fine. But that only lasted ten days and, once she'd gone back to her own cot, I loved being able to cuddle up to my partner again (without the huge bump) and without having to worry about her being in the bed with us. And now that she is in her own room, I love not having to creep into the bedroom any more so I don't wake her. Hopefully I'm saving myself from the trouble of a toddler who will only sleep if cuddled up to Mummy.
Leah from Bognor Regis, mum to Abbey, six months

My son was in a cot in our room until he was five months old, but as he was quite bad with colic and fed every two hours, he often ended up in bed with us on nights when he was really unsettled. Once he was in his own room, he still sometimes came in with us, if he was poorly or unsettled. And now he's older and in a big boy bed, he still wanders in occasionally, wanting to sleep with Mummy and Daddy. I must say, I love waking up next to him and am not against sharing a bed with your child in any way if it works for you. But I couldn't do it every night, as he's such a fidget.

Zoe from Rotherham, mum to Jack, one

Sam has always been a noisy sleeper and wriggles round non-stop so there's no way I would ever share a bed with him as I'd get no sleep at all! We sometimes bring him into our bed if he wakes early but he tends to get excited and jump all over us.

Isobel from London, mum to Sam, aged one

We had both of ours in bed with us. I breastfed both so it was easier and we just liked to be close to them. Our son has a double bed and sometimes asks me or his dad to get in with him, and sometimes our daughter comes in our bed. We don't mind where we sleep or who with. If we had a bed big enough I'm sure we'd all be in it.

Rebecca from Erith, mum to Harry, eight, and Mia, six

I had problems breastfeeding my son at first and learned to feed lying down, so we started bedsharing (my hubby took the sofa). After a couple of months I got a 'side-car' cot that fit snugly next to the bed, so that my son was beside me all night but in his own space. He continued to feed during the night until he was a year old, but stayed in his side-car until he was three, when he moved (happily) to his own room. His sister was born two months later and went straight into a side-car cot, too. I can feed at night with minimum disturbance, so get good sleep. I like being so close to her at night, especially as I'm now back at work full-time.

Heather from Canterbury, mum to Liam, three, and Niamh, six months

My eldest daughter suffered very badly with colic and reflux, and after six weeks of trying to get her to sleep in her cot beside our bed I gave up and brought her in with us, which really helped her settle. From then on she would go to bed in her cot and when she woke for her first feed I would take her in with us and she would stay there till morning. At seven months we moved her into her own room as we found we were disturbing her by turning over and she didn't seem to mind at all. I decided when our second daughter was born to take her in with us immediately and, despite feeding a lot during the night, she slept well between feeds. You definitely don't sleep as deeply when a tiny baby is in bed with you but I think you get more sleep than if you have to get up every two hours to feed! Now my eldest daughter almost never comes into bed with us as she likes her own bed best and my youngest is in every night. I really don't mind as long as we all get some sleep.

Yvonne from Aberdeen, mum to Hannah, four, and Eilidh, two

We have had a family bed and co-slept for years. Even when our kids were young babies I always had enough sleep. I would often go to bed at 8.30pm, my sleep was broken many times, but by morning I could total a good nine hours and I would feel great. I have never had any tears over bedtime, no need to use controlled crying, and my husband and I have been imaginative enough to maintain a healthy sex life – which doesn't always have to be conducted in the bed! I think babies and small children need lots of comfort, and when I look at my children now I can see how they've benefited. They left the bed when they were four or five but, even now, at 12 and nine, they both sometimes sleep with us if they want to top-up on cuddles; maybe once a month.

Sandra from Edinburgh, mum to Joseph, 12, and Joan, nine

My son, now five, never slept with us and was always put in his own cot from day one. He's a brilliant little sleeper and I don't feel that I missed out on any bonding. If anything, I feel closer to him as I slept well and didn't feel exhausted. My daughter, now two, always slept with us. It was easier at the start as I had a c-section with her and found it difficult to get up out of bed. But now she can't bear to sleep on her own. I wish I had been harder in the early days as she has never slept through in two years and I'm exhausted from her disturbing us. Her little bed is at the side of ours but she won't stay in it, and I'm too tired and too soft to do anything about it.

Andrea from Nottingham, mum to Harry, five, and Alice, two

I did everything by the book for the first two months and had her in a Moses basket next to my bed. Then, as I was breastfeeding, I decided it would be easier to have her in bed with me. My other half was very against it – we had arguments and he made me feel guilty. But she still slept with us and we never really had a bad night as a result. At two she went into a big bed, but on Friday nights she comes in with us. It's my favourite night of the week!

Karen from Swindon, mum to Lucy, three

We decided when I was pregnant that the baby would not be sleeping in our bed. We felt we needed to ensure he knew that our bed was *our* bed, and we also didn't want habits to form so decided not to start it in the first place! (I was still sleeping in my mum's bed at seven.) Not once has he slept with us. Our bed belongs to us, his belongs to him. Even now if I ask him to come in for a cuddle he'll be in and out in two minutes because he's just not used to it. He is also a very wriggly child and I wouldn't have been able to have any sleep at all because of this!

Dyanne from Fife, mum to Luke, four

I didn't have any thoughts on bedsharing before my son came along but from day one he was so clingy and I was so tired that he ended up sharing with us so I could sleep while he fed. For us it was safer, as I know that if I'd sat in a chair while holding him I would probably have dropped him. The problems this caused meant he wouldn't sleep without me and this lasted until he was about 18 months, when we used the gradual retreat sleep training method [see page 118]. With my daughter we made a decision not to let her sleep in our bed from the start. So after every feed I would put her in her cot and leave her. She certainly sleeps a lot better than my son.

Jenna from Wolverhampton, mum to Jude, three, and Arabella, nine months

3 Sleep solutions
for your newborn

How a newborn sleeps

You might be amazed how much your new baby sleeps at first, although like so many things, newborn sleep is very variable – on average, she'll spend up to 16 out of 24 hours asleep, for long stretches of up to four hours at a time. As with many of the facts and figures you'll read, this is only an average – *your* newborn may sleep more or less than that. And, in general, you don't have to worry at this stage whether she's getting enough or not, because newborns are good at taking what they need. (It might feel as though your baby is missing out on a lot of vital kip, but rest assured she'll be making up for it elsewhere in her day.)

In the early weeks, your baby won't sleep any more during the night than she does in the day. That's because newborns have yet to develop a functioning body clock – known as a circadian rhythm – so they have no concept of a difference between day and night. They also have very small stomachs, so for a while they simply can't go for more than a couple of hours without getting hungry. As a result, it's perfectly normal for a baby of up to three months to wake very frequently during the night – perhaps even as often as every hour, at first, looking for a feed or comfort. It can be hell but, at this stage, it's a question of coping as best you can: when they are this tiny, you really just have to pander to their needs and give them whatever they require to get back to sleep. The situation will improve over time, as their body clock begins to function and their tummy grows, allowing them to take bigger feeds at a time, which will sustain them for longer. Night-times should *definitely* be less of a nightmare by the time she's three months old and, even if they are not and she's still waking more than a couple of times a night, you can at least begin to take gentle steps to overcome the problem (see page 46) by then.

Should my baby be this *noisy*?

Another feature of newborn sleep that may surprise you is how noisy and erratic her breathing can seem. For many new parents it's a source of some worry and can lead to repeated checking to make sure their little one is still alive! But, as a general rule, it's normal and nothing to worry about. Babies breathe through their noses and so if your little one's nasal passages are blocked in any way or infected, you're going to hear about it. And pauses in the breath during sleep are also quite typical in the first month or so, as your baby learns to control her breathing. (Rarely, long pauses in breathing may indicate a condition called sleep apnoea, although this is far more likely to affect older babies and children. There's a bit more about it on page 167.)

Try not to let these things become a source of worry, but chat to your health visitor about it if you need reassurance. If you're anxious, you could try listening out for the sound of your baby's breathing by putting your ear close to her nose and mouth; looking closely at her chest and watching for the up and down movement of breathing; or putting your face next to hers and feeling her breath against your cheek. If still in any doubt about your baby's breathing – night or day – do check with your GP or give NHS Direct a call (numbers are included in the back of this book).

Cot death is very rare, thankfully. However, it goes without saying that if your baby appears to have stopped breathing for more than a short pause, and attempts to wake her fail, you should dial 999 and ask for an ambulance.

Going with the flow

Because of the erratic nature of newborn sleep, most parents find it easiest to let their baby sleep (and feed) as and when she wants during the first month to six weeks, at least, and to do whatever they need to settle her, or get her off to sleep. In other words, there's little point in worrying about strict routines or schedules, and no need to fret about setting up bad habits or sleep associations. There'll be plenty of time later to reverse them. Very young babies need loads of physical contact and reassurance from their parents, so don't be afraid to rock, cuddle or feed your newborn to sleep if it feels the right thing to do.

That said, there are still some simple measures you can take that are appropriate even now, which could help you forge good sleeping habits later – they're outlined a bit further on in this chapter, on page 46.

Rigid routine = contented baby?

Although most health professionals will tell you that a 'go-with-the-flow' approach is the best sleep solution for the early weeks, some baby sleep experts advocate a carefully planned routine for feeding and sleeping right from the very start. These sort of schedule-based methods of babycare are a little controversial. They take a lot of commitment and determination, and tend to be inflexible, sometimes making it tough to fit the rest of your life round them. There's also concern that they are not baby-centred enough. However, there's no doubt that a lot of parents swear by them. Only you can decide whether you've got the energy and focus to attempt a rigid routine so early on in your baby's life. And remember, if you do pick up one of these sorts of guides, many parents get good results by cherry-picking some bits of advice and discarding others – you may not *have* to follow one to the letter for it to work for you.

If you're taking the go-with-the-flow approach, bear in mind that more regular patterns of sleep and feeding tend to establish themselves quite naturally over time – and that there are lots of things you can do to encourage that process gently, such as establishing a good bedtime (see the following chapter for more on that). So even if you reject routine-based days and nights for your newborn, chances are you'll adopt them – and find them a great help – a bit later down the line.

Louise says: My feeling about strict routines for newborns is that they're only workable if you've got the right personality. You need to be very organised and very determined – perhaps even a bit hard. And if that's your take on life, then fair enough. But I know from experience that a lot of parents try them and find they just can't get them to work. And when that happens, it can really destroy your confidence. So my advice would be to use these approaches with caution, aiming to adapt it to suit rather than going entirely by the book. I also feel that those first few precious weeks are a time to get in tune with your baby, so you can begin to pick up subtle cues regarding their needs, and these sorts of books don't allow for this.

Maggie says: All little ones are different and some infants will obligingly slot into whatever routine you impose on them quite happily. However, child psychologists have concerns that for more sensitive babies, strict routines could be harmful as they don't encourage 'attuned parenting'. In the early days, mum, dad and baby are getting to know one another and it's really important that parents become sensitive to their babies' cues and learn to respond sensitively to them. If these social cues are not responded to with empathy, it can interfere with the natural bonding and attachment process.

What the netmums say

Rigid routines versus go-with-the-flow

I didn't have any set plan when I was pregnant with my son; I just thought that if we could survive day to day then I was doing well. However, as he grew, we did get him into a routine that fitted our family life, and when my daughter was born, she just sort of slotted into it, too.
Gail from Glasgow, mum to Brodie, seven, and Zoe, six

A friend bought me a routine-based parenting book and I read it when I was pregnant. I started following the advice and put my son to sleep in a cot from birth. When Max was around two months old we moved and in the first week we

had to sleep together as his cot was not up. It was so nice and so much easier to feed him that I left him in my bed and we still co-sleep now. I'm sorry I didn't do it sooner.
Anna from Upper Edmonton, mum to Max, 11 months

It's all a bit of a haze now, but the first few weeks were horrific. I was a bit anti-strict-schedule but, having nothing else to turn to, I did pick it up and installed my own routine (of sorts) just to get me through each day.
Julie from London, mum to Edith, five months

I am and always have been a big believer in routine and planned from the start to follow Gina Ford's theories. Friends and relatives all insisted that routines don't work, and babies should set the pace. But they ate their words when my daughter was sleeping soundly all night from eight weeks, with a two-hour nap during the day. Needless to say, I am still a big believer in routine.
Melissa from Lancaster, mum to Annabelle, one

We didn't have a routine in the early weeks with either of my sons. I remember thinking I should have one when our first son was born, but I never seemed to be able to stick to the timings. It got me stressed out more than anything, so I decided to forget about routines and just go with the flow. It worked wonders for me! We didn't have a set bedtime during the early weeks. I was breastfeeding and he would often be downstairs in the lounge with us until we went to bed. Sometimes I gave him his late evening feed while watching TV. Sometimes I would feed him in our bed before transferring him into the carrycot (he wouldn't sleep in his crib!). He was a

great sleeper – unlike my younger son who woke almost every
hour for a feed in the early weeks.
Irma from Oldham, mum to Damir, two, and Aydin, eight months

Coping with sleep deprivation

Lots of first-time parents feel shocked – and even depressed – by
how much they get woken at night by their newborn baby. The
amount of time spent awake at night stacks up further if your baby
takes an age to settle back to sleep again, or if you're an exclusively
breastfeeding mum (and, therefore, it's always you that must be on
call throughout the night).

On the plus side, new babies sleep loads during the day. Use this
time, whenever possible, to catch up on some sleep yourself (and
yes, the laundry won't get done by itself, but put aside whatever
non-essential housework you can). Be sure to draw on any help you
get offered, by your partner, or willing friends or relatives, too.
Anyone who has also been through this period of life will know how
you're feeling and sympathise – capitalise on that by jumping at the
chance should they offer to babysit for a couple of hours, or perhaps
even a whole night, when that becomes feasible.

Some mums find that ordinary sleep deprivation is compounded by
insomnia – so, frustratingly, even when their baby has dropped off
again, they cannot. It's usually caused by anxiety, which plagues many
new parents. And as overtiredness can (ironically) make getting to
sleep harder, it can easily become a vicious circle. Both insomnia and
exhaustion can be symptoms of postnatal depression so if you're really
struggling, do talk it through with a sympathetic health professional.
But generally speaking, lack of sleep is simply one of the drawbacks of
having a new baby. And during this challenging period, it's usually a
question of coping as best you can until you're through it.

Tips on coping with sleep deprivation

- Eat well: keeping your body well-fuelled will help you keep going when exhaustion strikes during the day. It's also really important if you're breastfeeding because you need a full complement of calories to keep your milk supplies up. You may not have the time or energy to cook elaborate meals at this point, but try to snack healthily, at the very least, on sandwiches made from wholemeal bread, jacket potatoes with easy fillings, and nutritious nibbles such as cheese and fruit. If you're struggling to sleep in between being woken by your baby, try eating foods rich in tryptophan, a naturally occurring sedative: these include turkey, bananas, pasta, potato and hot milk. A good intake of calcium could also help (for good sources, see page 175) – as well as being a particularly important nutrient for breastfeeding mums, it's known to be a natural tranquilliser.

- Avoid too much caffeine: don't overload on tea, coffee and cola in the day to keep you going; it's likely to make you feel worse in the long run. And don't be tempted to booze excessively in the hope it will help you sleep. It will only make you feel worse when you have to get up in the night and, besides, you need your wits about you when caring for a baby. It could also, if you're breastfeeding, affect your baby for the worse.

- Take some gentle regular exercise: although it might sound like the more exhausting option than doing nothing, a little exercise will help boost your energy levels and help you to cope. Don't try anything strenuous in the first few months after birth; gentle walking with your baby in the buggy or sling is ideal (with the added advantage that fresh air can help both you and your baby to sleep better).

- Sleep in the day when you can. 'Power naps' can be very effective: even if you feel dreadful when you wake up after a 15-minute kip, you'll feel the benefit later.

- If napping is out of the question, take some time to rest and relax every day – even if only for ten minutes. Try a spot of yoga, or just some simple deep breathing. Essential oils, such as lavender or ylang ylang, added to a warm bath can be a great help. Enjoy a cuppa, listen to some music, speak to a friend via phone or email, log on to Netmums, watch telly, or read a magazine, paper or book. And spend at least a few moments each day appreciating the good things you *do* have in your life . . .

- Go to bed as early as possible so you can at least catch up on a good chunk of sleep early on in the night.

- Make sure your partner pulls his weight during the night (it's no excuse that you're on maternity leave and he's got to go to work the following day – you've got a tiring day ahead of you, too). If you're breastfeeding you could try expressing sometimes (it's best to wait a good month or so before offering your baby a bottle, but a good idea to try as soon as possible after that, before your baby becomes unreceptive to the idea) so you can build up supplies for your other half to do the feeds some nights. If you're alone, you won't have such a luxury: but even the odd uninterrupted night's sleep will refresh you, so ask a good friend or close relative to come over and help with the night shift every now and then.

- Try to see the situation as a short-term problem. Your baby will almost certainly be sleeping for longer stretches within a few months and, even if she isn't, there'll come a time when you can take steps to help her do so. (And by six months, there's nothing stopping you from getting a whole night's sleep if you want to, as explained in chapter five). Meanwhile, turn the clock to the wall and try not to obsess about sleep – or your lack of it!

Maggie says: Experts still do not know the exact causes of postnatal depression (PND), but it's thought broken sleep and exhaustion are contributory factors. Even a straightforward birth experience can be a huge challenge for a woman's body, so if it was difficult or prolonged it can be overwhelming. Years ago women used to have a 'lying-in' period after childbirth and a large extended family to help. Nowadays we're often expected to bounce out of hospital after 24 hours and carry on with our normal life, which is unrealistic. We need to give ourselves time to adjust to motherhood, a different dynamic in our relationship with our partner, the loss of our independence, our new role and, in many cases, the prospect of living on one salary. All this to deal with – and lack of sleep, too. We need to be very gentle on ourselves at this time.

What the netmums say

Coping with sleep deprivation

It was only three and a bit months before my baby slept a solid 12 hours, but it was another month or so before I did! If I had done any more than that I seriously think I would have gone bonkers – I found myself snapping at everyone over the stupidest things, and being really tearful and stressed. I am very ashamed to admit that I said to my partner on more than one occasion when I was woken by the baby crying to just drop him out of the window, or chuck him down the stairs. I know that's awful but it's really how bad the lack of sleep made me feel at the time. Of course I would *never* have done it, although looking back I don't remember thinking straight at all for those first few months. I think we all hear about sleep deprivation before we have our babies but we don't realise what it is actually like until you get there.

Chrissie from Bolton, mum to Freddie, one

For three months after my son was born I either had literally no sleep at all, or about three hours a day – he still wanted comfort after breastfeeding and hated to be put down. Some quality sleep only came when I stopped breastfeeding at five months and we moved him into his own room, at which point he actually went to sleep on his own. My pattern of sleep never improved, though, as I think my body had got used to just three hours. Some nights I would be manic doing housework, as I could never switch off. Eventually I was diagnosed with PND. I also felt quite physically unwell and the doctor said my immune system was low. I think lack of sleep was a factor in both.

Melanie from Manchester, mum to Matthew, two

Sleep deprivation turned me into a complete mess after my first baby. She had colic and would be up for hours on end during the night, screaming. Then once her colic was sorted I found I could no longer sleep properly. I couldn't get to sleep for fear of her waking and crying, and would lie awake until 5am. I'd be like a zombie the next day and was so overtired and fearful of not sleeping the next night that I couldn't get to sleep for worrying about it. I used to dread bedtime as I knew that the cycle would start again. I started having anxiety attacks while trying to get to sleep, my heart would beat so fast and hard I thought it would burst out of my chest. I barely slept for weeks and was a gibbering wreck. Eventually I had to go to the doctor for sleeping tablets, which helped break the vicious cycle I was in. I now find that, with a four-year-old and a one-year-old, I don't need any extra help to get to sleep these days – I'm shattered enough by bedtime! But, when I look back, those were very dark days. Thank goodness they are over.

Rachel from Rossendale, mum to Jessica, four, and Thomas, one

Having a supportive husband really helps, sharing the load and grabbing some sleep when you can. I used to nap when my son did and I couldn't have got through the nights without that. Forget about the cooking and cleaning – if folk come round, ask them to help!

Sarah from Edinburgh, mum to Jack, 11 months

Setting up good habits from the start

Even in the very early days, there are some things you can do which will help pave the way for good sleep habits later. For example, you can:

- Help your baby understand the difference between night and day. You can do this by keeping the lights low, avoiding eye contact and being silent and businesslike when feeding and changing her at night. Likewise, you should be as chatty and sociable as possible during the day. It's a good idea to differentiate daytime naps from night-time sleep, too – putting your baby down for daytime sleeps in a room that isn't too dark, for instance, or settling her in a carrycot or pram in the hallway, or a room downstairs.

- Try to make it a habit, early on, to put your baby into her own Moses basket or cot for sleeping at night and for at least some of her naps, so she learns that it's a happy place to be. Some babies object to this at first, but it's important to persevere: lovely as it can be to have her fall asleep on your chest or lap, she may end up refusing to go to sleep anywhere else. It could also be dangerous, as falling asleep on a chair or sofa with your baby is a major cot death risk. Of course, it's fine for her to nap sometimes in her pram, sling or car seat if that's where she dropped off – but not all the time, or she might become reliant on one of those conditions to fall asleep.

- Try, even if it's only sometimes, to make sure she's still awake when you put her down for a sleep. You'll be taking the first steps in teaching her the vital skill of self-settling – there's lots more about this in the following chapter, on page 76.

- Get her used to a certain amount of background noise when she's sleeping and don't tiptoe round her. If your baby always needs total silence in order to get to sleep, it will become a difficult condition to maintain!

- Take your baby out and about in the daylight every day. Research shows that this can aid the development of the body clock and improve a baby's sleep at night because it boosts production of melatonin, a hormone that promotes sleep.

- Don't instantly jump up to attend to your baby if she stirs at night, or in the middle of a nap. Leave her for a few moments. It's always possible she'll drop off again, anyway.
- By all means start a bedtime routine as early as you want – experts agree it's one of the best ways to encourage your baby to settle and sleep well. However, there's probably not a lot of point doing so much before six weeks, because a baby's sleep/awake patterns are so unsettled this early on and because many tend to feed more than usual in the evenings. There's a lot more on bedtime routines in the following chapter.

What the netmums say

Setting up good habits from the start

My tip is: start as you mean to go on. It's very easy to slip into bad habits like rocking to sleep or bringing the baby into your bed but these habits are then hard to break and cause upset to all involved. From the day my youngest son was born I've always fed him, then swaddled him and put him into his bed awake. He drops off by himself with no help from me. He's slept from 7am to 7pm with a dream feed [see page 82] at 10ish since he was four to five weeks old.
Louvaine from Rickmansworth, mum to Josh, seven, Caitlin, five, Isabel, four, Oliver, three, and Noah, three months

If you start putting them down while they are still awake and leave them to fall asleep on their own right from the beginning (however tempting newborn hugs are!), they learn that falling asleep alone in their own cot is normal and will not stress them out or panic them. It's extremely hard to do this; we all know how much we never want to let them go when they are tiny babes (especially first babies, as we have all the time in the world to spend just staring at these beautiful beings who we have created!). But it's in their best interests in the long run.

Zoe from Exeter, mum to Baylee, seven, Coco, five, and Lexee, two

This is our first baby so we don't really know what we're doing! But from about three weeks I've tried to make night-time different from daytime. She does not like to be swaddled, but loves a dummy. I try to put her in her Moses basket when she's awake but sometimes she falls asleep when feeding so this doesn't always happen. I don't think she's doing too badly at sleeping but she generally wakes for a feed every three hours or so. I have no idea when sleeping through the night will happen, but we're going to try and get her into a bedtime routine sometime soon.

Kate from Leeds, mum to Megan, two months

I think there's a lot of luck involved as to whether you have a baby that sleeps well – or doesn't – and we've been fairly lucky. But I also think there's a lot you can do from the start to 'mould them'. In the very early days our son was quite colicky and preferred to sleep resting on either my shoulder or my husband's and, if you tried to move him, he woke up. Also, the early evening was just constant feeding, from about 7–11pm and it was totally knackering. But swaddling was definitely useful in the early days, as was persevering with a routine, which we introduced as early as possible. And keeping calm helps!

Sarah from Edinburgh, mum to Jack, 11 months

Should I give my baby a comforter?

Many parents find that a comforter in the form of a dummy, or an object such as a blanket, hankie, or a small, age-appropriate soft toy, is a useful aid in helping their baby settle. A routinely given comforter (psychologists often call them 'transitional objects') can provide familiarity and security if cuddled up to – and can become just as satisfactory as Mum or Dad in soothing and giving comfort to a little one, helping them to drop off without you around. And it doesn't really matter what the object is – so although there's a range of ready-made comforters on the market, a small square of muslin or cellular blanket is just as likely to gain favour.

Comforters do come with some drawbacks, mainly the problem of what happens when your baby can't find hers during the night (and will probably wake you to help her find it!). There is also the possibility of a major habit developing in the long-term, which, if sucking is involved, could expose her to bacteria and potentially affect speech and language development, as well as affect her adult teeth. If you do want to offer your baby a comforter, bear in mind the following:

- Don't offer a dummy in the first four weeks or so if you're breastfeeding, in case it interferes with your baby's ability to suck at the breast. Sterilise dummies regularly to help guard against increased risk of infections, replace them if they become cracked or damaged, and never coat them in anything sweet.
- If you give your baby a dummy at night, make sure you give it to her every night. Give it to her whenever she needs settling, but don't worry about replacing it if it falls out when she's asleep, and never force her to take it.

- Have at least one spare available. Serious problems could arise if your baby's comforter gets lost!

- Be prepared to get up in the night to find your baby's comforter if she's dropped it or it falls out and this causes her to wake up. (If your baby's comforter is a dummy, you could try a 'soother saver' – a clip that you can use to attach a dummy to your baby's sleepsuit. You could also do as some mums advise and put lots of dummies in the cot within her reach, so your baby has a good chance of grabbing one.)

- A cloth comforter can have extra appeal if it has your 'smell' on it. You could try keeping it tucked in your bra for a few hours a day, when she doesn't need it. If you're breastfeeding, a used cloth breastpad can have a similarly comforting effect.

- Consider weaning your baby off her comforter after six months if you want to avoid a long-term, hard-to-break habit developing – it's easier to stop now than later and, if you are sleep training (see page 103), it can work well to drop it at the same time.

- Restrict comfort objects to sleeping and soothing times. As long as you do this, there are no risks attached and it really doesn't matter how long they cling on to them! (They'll drop it – eventually – of their own accord.)

Thumb and finger sucking

If your baby takes to sucking her thumb or fingers as a means of soothing and settling herself, she may not need a comfort object at all and, unlike a dummy, blanket or toy, she will never lose it and you'll never have to get up to replace it! In fact, some people say it's a good idea to encourage a baby to adopt this particular habit early on, by gently placing her thumb or fingers in her mouth. On the other hand, finger or thumb sucking can be a harder habit to give up since, unlike dummies, a child's digits can't simply be taken away! Generally speaking, though, if your baby is going to adopt this method of self-settling, she will, so there's no point in fretting about it becoming an undesirable and long-term habit. Chances are, she'll have dropped or at least reduced the habit before it could have an effect on her permanent teeth.

Louise says: There's no right or wrong when it comes to comfort objects and thumb sucking. A much-loved object can certainly be instantly calming for them. The downside is that, at some point, you'll have to get rid of it – although that can be done easily enough later on. There's no harm in helping them to find their thumb or fingers to suck either but, on the whole, if they're going to do this, they'll do it with or without your help. As I recall, my daughter sucked her palm to settle herself!

Maggie says: My feeling about dummies, in particular, is that, while often a lifesaver in the early months, they are best ditched from six months because I think they can end up causing more sleep problems than they solve, as parents end up having to get up in the night in order to replace them!

What the netmums say

Dummies and other comforters

With both my boys I used a very thin cotton blanket which I'd kept on me for a few hours before bedtime so that they could be comforted by my smell. My first had this tied to his cot and my second held it and still does! I made sure they knew this was just for bedtime to save it becoming a serious daytime habit, too. I also put them to bed while awake so they could learn to fall asleep on their own and, to this day, both of them sleep from 7pm to 6.30am, so it's worked well for us!

Hazel from Putney, mum to Leo, three, and Chase, one

My babies had dummies from day one and I found they really helped to settle them to sleep and get them back to sleep if they woke. I recall with my eldest feeling like I shouldn't be giving her a dummy – I used to whip it out if anyone came near the pram! – but as soon as I introduced it she was like a changed child. They've caused no problems as far as I'm concerned and I'd encourage other new mums to try one if they're struggling to settle their baby. I've always been careful to restrict them. Jessica gave hers up without a struggle and Thomas has his just for sleep times now. The only bugbear is when they get lost. When they've woken in the night looking for it, one of us has always gone in to replace it. We didn't mind this, though, and they'd always be back to sleep in minutes.

Rachel from Rossendale, mum to Jessica, four, and Thomas, one

My eldest didn't have a comforter and I used to find her hard to settle. When my middle one was born, I started giving her a terry nappy to hold and she soon became attached to it. She was only really interested in it for sleep time, so it never became a problem later on, although it's provided reassurance during many situations such as doctor's appointments or during immunisations. She's now five and still goes to bed with a terry nappy, as does her younger sister – who I deliberately gave one, too, from the start, as I knew what a life-saver it had been!

Zoe from Exeter, mum to Baylee, seven, Coco, five, and Lexee, two

We've used dummies both times from very early on. The first time she was inconsolable and I didn't know what else to try. She drifted off to sleep with the dummy, though, and it definitely helped her settle. This time it is the same, but I've found one huge drawback. The dummy keeps falling out, and you have to get up and put it back in. But I'd prefer that to her sucking her hands. At least a dummy can be taken away when she's older.

Kathleen from Hamilton, mum to Rachael, three, and Elena, one month

Cluster feeding

Breastfeeding mums often find that their newborn wants to 'cluster feed' in the course of an evening – in other words, is keen to take longer feeds and more frequently than usual – and it's a good idea to go along with this demand, as it can help fill their tummies and buy you a little more sleep in the night. Formula-fed babies are less likely to require extra, as formula is more filling. In any case, a baby should never be urged to take more milk than they seem to want in the hope it will encourage sleep. And it's certainly not a good idea to add extra formula to the bottle for the same purpose, as this could lead to your baby becoming constipated, and may even put her at risk – later on – of obesity.

Is it ok to swaddle my baby?

The age-old practice of swaddling a newborn – in other words, wrapping her up tightly in a sheet or blanket, with limbs firmly enclosed – is still recommended by many babycare experts and professionals, particularly for premature babies. In fact, swaddling has had a resurgence in popularity recently, having gone out of favour a few decades ago due to fears it restrained a baby's freedom of movement and might hamper their development. Swaddling is said to aid sleep and help a baby feel calm, relaxed and secure, as it mimics the conditions of the womb and restricts the instinctive, jerky movements that babies make. There's no doubt that lots of parents find it a useful technique.

However, in a major recent study, a possible association was made between swaddling and an increased risk of cot death – in contrast to previous beliefs that swaddling *improved* safety as it can help keep babies on their backs. As yet, there is no official advice *not to* swaddle. But it's probably a good idea, if you try it, to bear in mind the following tips:

- Make sure you are swaddling your baby in the right way. You want your baby to be firmly wrapped so she can't wriggle out and become cold, or risk getting her head covered, but it's also important that the swaddle is not *too* tight. Ask your health visitor to demonstrate how it's done.
- To avoid overheating and allow your baby some freedom, always leave her arms out when you swaddle.
- Remember that some babies like to be swaddled and others do not. If you do try it, yours will soon let you know how she feels either way.

- If there *is* an increased cot death risk from swaddling, it's likely to be due to overheating. Advice from the Foundation for the Study of Infant Death Syndrome (FSID) is that if you *do* swaddle your baby, be sure her head is not covered and make sure the covering you use is a thin material. A cotton sheet is ideal. You can also now choose from a whole range of lightweight blankets specifically marketed for swaddling, including some with Velcro fasteners to help you put them on properly. If it's a cold time of year, you may have to add another light blanket or two during sleep. Use common sense to decide what she needs in the way of extra layers – and check regularly to make sure she's not getting too hot or becoming chilly. The FSID advises against putting a swaddled baby in a sleeping bag.
- Only swaddle your baby for the first two to three months – after that, she will need more freedom to move and develop.
- Giving your baby a sleeping bag is a good alternative to swaddling, as it provides warmth and security, but gives your baby plenty of scope to move.

Soothing an unsettled baby

Most newborns need nothing more than a big feed and a good burp or a cuddle from a warm, willing adult, to settle them to sleep in the early weeks. But for some, it's not so simple. Up to a fifth of babies suffer from the common problem of colic (see below), and it's a fact that some newborns are just very sensitive and cranky at the start of life – perhaps because of the physical or emotional consequences of a traumatic birth; maybe due to the shock of their expulsion from a cosy womb into a bright, loud outside world; or possibly just because that's the personality your baby was born with. When this is the case, you'll just have to do whatever you can to offer her comfort and get her to sleep as best you can.

Coping with colic

Up to a fifth of babies suffer from infant colic – prolonged bouts of excessive crying – during the first three to four months. There's no real cure (although there are preparations such as Infacol and Colief available from the chemist, which some mums report can help) and it's not known for certain what causes it, although pain caused by an immature digestive system is one of the main theories. As it typically occurs late in the evening, it can be a major problem for parents who are trying to settle a newborn baby to sleep for the night. And, as most people will resort to anything in their desperation to soothe a colic-stricken child, it can lead to a fair few dodgy sleep associations being set up – and may also be a real sticking point when it comes to trying to teach self-settling (see page 76) or establishing a peaceful bedtime (page 71), since a distressed, colic-stricken baby may only settle in a vibrating chair, or simply won't go to sleep unless you are walking up and down the hallway with her in your arms.

If you're affected by colic, use whatever method of settling gets you a result until the phase passes (there are some suggestions in the box below), which is almost always within three to four months. Once the evening crying passes, you can take steps to introduce a bedtime, and any 'unhelpful' sleep associations that your baby has become accustomed to can either be gently removed over a period of time, or – if you wait until she's six months old or more – dispensed with at the same time as sleep training (see chapter five).

Solutions for settling an unsettled baby

- Check for all the obvious problems – is she hungry, thirsty, too hot, too cold, in need of a nappy change, poorly?

- Take her for a walk in the pram or keep her close to you in a sling.

- Put her in her car seat and take her for a drive.

- Hold, cuddle, jiggle or rock her in your arms.

- Sing to her or play her music. Research shows Brahms and Bach to be particularly effective!

- Let her listen to the 'white noise' of a washing machine or vacuum cleaner. You could also try playing recordings of 'womb music'.

- Give her a warm bath.

- Offer her a herbal preparation of one teaspoon of camomile, fennel, or peppermint tea (available from health food shops and some chemists) diluted in a bottle of water. Or drink a cup yourself, if you're breastfeeding.

- Swaddle your baby (see the box above for some important safety tips).

- Allow her to suck on your breast or a dummy (for more on dummies see page 50).

- Try a spot of baby massage. It can help if you gently push your baby's legs up to her chest, or move them round in a 'bicycling' motion.

- Walk up and down the stairs with her in your arms. Some babies are soothed by the upwards/downwards motion.

- Give a vibrating or rocking chair/crib a whirl.

- Look into cranial osteopathy. There's no evidence that this alternative technique definitely works, but many who try it report great success. There's a bit more about this and other alternative practices on page 172.

Louise says: Some babies just take time getting used to the world, and they need a lot of help or comfort from you to settle. Do whatever it takes and, remember, when it comes to helping them get to sleep, you can't really make mistakes this early on in your baby's life so don't beat yourself up if that's what you feel you are doing – it can all be turned around! Colic, in particular, can cause a very difficult scenario but the sad truth is there's very little you can do about it. Your baby will grow out of it but, in the meantime, do whatever you (safely) can to settle your baby and preserve your sanity.

Other medical causes for problems settling

Occasionally, babies with colicky symptoms who won't settle or go to sleep easily may be suffering from a medical problem such as a milk allergy or lactose intolerance, or gastro-oesophageal reflux, so it's worth getting them ruled out by your GP. There's more about these in chapter seven.

Bear in mind, too, that if the crying is accompanied by symptoms such as vomiting, diarrhoea, failure to gain weight, fever (a temperature of 38 degrees centigrade or more), constipation or dry nappies, your baby may be poorly and you should seek prompt medical attention.

When the going gets tough

Relentless crying is hard to cope with at the best of times. But if it's at night-time and you are exhausted, it can be unbearable. If things get to the point where you are unable to cope and you are worried you might hurt your baby as a result, put her in a completely safe place and leave her crying for a while until you feel calmer. If your partner or some other reliable adult is around, get them to take over. Otherwise, grab a cup of tea or a glass of wine if necessary (stick to no more than one or two units when you're in charge of a little one, and particularly if you're breastfeeding) and take five minutes. She'll be fine without you for a few moments.

The number for Cry-sis – a charity that supports parents in this sort of situation – is included at the back of this book.

What the netmums say

Soothing an unsettled baby

Both my babies suffered colic and it was just horrible trying to deal with it. The second time wasn't as bad as the first, as at least I knew what I was dealing with – and that it would all come to an end eventually, which it did, both times, at around three months. My eldest often cried well into the night, and my husband and I spent many hours trying to soothe her to sleep. It was horrendous at the time, but I look back now and it's no more than a distant memory. We sleep trained both our girls at six months and, to this day, they both sleep soundly all night.

Julia from Milton Keynes, mum to Nina, five, and Ellie, three

Mya had bad colic for the first four months so she basically just fell asleep on us after rocking or feeding her. Once it had passed we sorted her routine out – dinner, a bit of a play and some books, then bath, dressed for bed and into her cot. She seems to settle really easily. It's nice to have our evenings back to ourselves!

Kate from Leeds, mum to Mya, seven months

If you have a baby with colic then all the other sleep advice goes out of the window until the phase passes. My first baby cried *every* night from 6pm to midnight without a break. It was an incredibly tough time for all three of us and, even though she's eight now, I can still remember the despair of those first three months. With no family to help out we had to take it in shifts to cope. I slept in the day when she slept as much as I could and the nights themselves were not too bad, although we were exhausted by the time she finally settled at midnight. Surprisingly, after three months, she was a good sleeper. We gave her a blanket and she used to suck her thumb and we always put her in her cot awake, and she soon slept well and has continued to do so ever since. I think we all need to find what works for us and our babies and our family situations.

Nicola from Banbury, mum to Sadie, eight, Lola, five, and Johnny, two

I had a terribly colicky first baby and nothing worked until cranial osteopathy was suggested to me, when she was nine weeks. She had two 'treatments' over two weeks and she was cured. It was all quite amazing and I would absolutely recommend it to anyone. My second baby didn't have colic and was a great sleeper from day one, but I do think that swaddling, which I didn't do with my first, helped this and I would always do this again. As soon as he was swaddled he fell asleep and stayed asleep! Both had dummies, which I'm sure also helped.

Rachel from Rossendale, mum to Jessica, four, and Thomas, one

Babies born too soon

Premature babies (those born before 37 weeks) need sleep even more than other babies do, to boost their growth, appetite and general health. However, the development of their body clock (and, hence, more regular sleep patterns) will naturally occur later than in a full-term baby and they are also likely to feed even more frequently at first, as their stomachs are so small.

Maggie says: Because of their special needs, you may find you need to take a 'go-with-the-flow' approach for longer with a prem baby than you would with a full-term baby. On the other hand, babies often come out of special care units with fairly well established feed and sleep schedules in place, in which case, exploit the advantage by keeping them up at home. Swaddling [see page 55] can also be a helpful way of settling a prem baby, as it mimics the security of the womb, but a baby sleeping bag is a good alternative – just make sure you get the appropriate size. Once home, don't forget to put your baby down to sleep on her back, even if she's got used to sleeping on her front in hospital. It's a really important factor in reducing the risk of cot death. It's also advisable to avoid bedsharing with a prem baby [see page 27].

Sleep solutions for twins

Setting up good sleep habits for twins can be pretty challenging, but it's even more important to do so if you want to avoid a double dose of sleep problems long into the future.

- Go with the flow in the early weeks. Do whatever it takes to survive the experience.
- Try to get your babies on similar schedules as soon as you can, by putting them down for their night-time and daytime sleep at the same time (and, wherever possible, feeding them simultaneously, too). Many parents of multiples find it's a good policy to wake the other twin when one wakes for a feed in the night – although this goes against the usual rule about not waking a sleeping baby, it can be the only way to get some decent chunks of sleep. However, some parents of multiples prefer to treat their babies as individuals, pursuing separate routines if necessary – it's certainly common to find that one baby sleeps better than the other. You may just have to experiment to see what suits you best.
- Let your babies sleep together at first – they've grown used to each other's company in the womb, so it can help to calm and reassure them. If you have a large cot, and you follow all the usual safe-sleeping guidelines (see page 22), it is fine to put them in side-by-side, but it's not a good idea to put them together in a crib or Moses basket. An alternative approach is to invest in a special cot divider that allows them to sleep feet-to-feet. For safety reasons you should put them in separate cots once they've started to roll over. Some parents find their multiples are easier to

settle if they are kept close together, others say if you've got the space, you'll get more sleep by separating them.

- All the usual rules apply with twins – in fact, they are doubly important! Set up a bedtime routine (see page 71) and teach them both to self-settle (see page 76) as soon as is feasible. After an exhausting day caring for two of them, you're even more likely to need the evening to yourself.

- Always tend to the twin who's making the least fuss first. The 'noisy' one will soon learn to wait. Don't immediately jump up to attend to one twin in the fear the other will wake. Allow some time for them to settle on their own first – the other twin may not wake up and, even if she does, she may not be bothered.

- Swaddling can be comforting for twins, who are accustomed to a tight squeeze in the womb. Check out page 55, though, for some important safety guidelines.

- Twins can be sleep trained using any of the usual methods [see page 103]. Chances are you will only need to train one of your twins, rather than both but, in any case, you may need to put them in separate rooms if you plan to undertake a potentially noisy method such as controlled crying (although you may be amazed at how much noise a twin will sleep through!). If you need to, you can sleep train twins simultaneously: you may need to be prepared for a more frequently disturbed night if they're on different waking schedules or – assuming you've got a partner on board – you could take a twin each!

- Mums of multiples need lots of specialist advice. Seek it from a relevant support organisation like Tamba, Twins UK or the Multiple Births Foundation – details are included in the back of the book.

What the netmums say

Coping with two at a time

I fed Zac and Tiggy a lot during the night for their first six months. I tried to reduce the number of times I was being woken by waking the other one up for a feed after feeding the one that had woken me. They had formula for their dream feed [see page 82], which usually gave me four hours' sleep, then I breastfed them during the rest of the night, so I was woken every two hours or so from that point. The turning point was at six months when they were moved into separate rooms (Zac is a fairly light sleeper). By then they were fully weaned and on three meals a day, and suddenly they stopped waking me for feeds. I suspect that, with Zac in particular, he was only half waking up, being disturbed by my husband (I find it hard to sleep with him myself, at times) and then crying, so I would feed him. Without the disturbance of being in the same room as us, they started to sleep through naturally and have done so most nights since.

Fiona from Birmingham, mum to Tiggy and Zac, one

We have never had much sleep, really, and our girls are now two. Much of this is due to dummy dependence as a sleep crutch. At four months old I reduced their dummy use to sleep times only – and inadvertently created a huge problem for myself. They now won't sleep without one. We're about to give the dummies to the 'baby reindeer', though – and are talking about it with them lots, which seems to be quite well accepted. My top tip for getting through the early days and sleep with multiples is that if one wakes for feeding, always wake the other for a feed, too.

Otherwise you can guarantee that as soon as you've settled back into bed, the unfed child will wake! We co-slept our girls in the same cot, which seemed to keep them more settled than when they were separated. Even now, their toddler beds need to be up next to each other.
Chessy from Windsor, mum to Holly and Poppy, two

My twins were born one minute apart, with Charlie weighing just over 5lb and Billy just over 4lb. What a difference that one pound made. Billy had reflux so was always being sick and fed hourly for about five months, all day and most of the night, while Charlie was a good feeder. I was up most of the night and it was such hard work. At five months Charlie went into his own room and generally slept through the night really well, he also napped well during the day. Billy, who went into his cot in the room with Charlie at six months, wouldn't nap much and would then end up overtired and awake until late in the evening. At 15 months, Charlie would be in bed by 8pm and sleep until 7am, Billy would fall asleep after a bottle but wake and scream as soon as I put him in the cot. Like idiots we would bring him back downstairs so as not to wake Charlie, and he would then be up and on the go until 1am. Finally, at about 18 months, we'd had enough of Billy's antics and decided to put him to bed and let him cry it out. He cried for about half an hour and then went to sleep! They are now in bed at 6pm and sleep through till 6.30am. I can't remember the early days of their life as it all passed in a completely exhausted blur. My advice is to get twins into a routine as early as possible. Don't give in and let them sleep in your bed. Been there and done it. Big mistake!
Michelle from Romford, mum to Charlie and Billy, two

It's definitely worth persevering with a routine for twins. I used Gina Ford's, having had it work for my daughter. Jacob slept through at three months and Felix a couple of weeks later. Felix is an early riser, though – anything from 5.30am – but thankfully doesn't usually wake his brother who sleeps in the same room. We put them in different Moses baskets and then in different cots but in their own room as soon as we brought them home. Felix just needs less sleep than Jacob and I've had to accept that. His lunchtime nap is only ever an hour whereas Jacob will do two. The key thing is to have a routine and an indicator that it's sleep time: I have always recited the same rhyme, just before putting them down.

Rachel from Hildenborough, mum to Esther, three, and Felix and Jacob, nine months

We've always had sleep issues and I think we just cope now because we're used to having so little sleep. My daughter slept like a dream from six weeks, but how different my two little fellas are! We've mastered the bedtime routine now and they go to sleep without any fuss after bath time, story, milk, but no matter what time we put them to bed, they still wake up at around 4.30am! We've tried everything – naps in the day, no naps, long walks, late evening snack, putting them down later in the night, trainer clocks, reward charts and bribery! They have to share a room because we don't have another bedroom. I don't think it gets easier; I think you just get used to having less sleep. I would love for someone to have them overnight just once, so I could have a lie-in!

Ghislaine from Leeds, mum to Alannah, six, and Ciabhan and Cormac, three

4 Sleep solutions
from six weeks to six months

Things can only get better . . . !

At some point during this period your baby will almost certainly become more settled, with more regular patterns of feeding and sleeping establishing themselves naturally. He'll start to nap for shorter periods in the day and sleep for longer stretches at night. In particular, three months typically proves a real turning point. By then, his body clock has regulated and his levels of melatonin, the sleep hormone, have increased. And if you've been dealing with the misery of colic and relentless crying, it will fade to an unhappy memory as his digestive system matures and the shock of life outside the womb eases.

Some lucky parents report that their babies are 'sleeping through' from as early as six weeks, but don't feel disheartened at this sort of boast if your little one seems a very long way off that. These people (assuming they aren't exaggerating) are definitely in a small minority! It's early days, so if you're still being woken several times a night, bear in mind that that's perfectly normal. In fact, many babies simply won't start sleeping through of their own accord – they need help to achieve it, which is where you come in. (And, incidentally, you may be heartened to hear that professionals generally classify a stretch of six hours or more as 'sleeping through'. So perhaps you're closer than you think – or are even there already.)

What the netmums say

Turning a corner

The first two nights were hell; he didn't sleep for longer than an hour at a time. After that, he slept from around 10.30 pm, after his last bottle, until waking for a feed at 3am, and then straight back to bed until around eight. Then, when he was about eight weeks, he began sleeping through all night, from about 10pm until seven. I feel that getting him into that routine early on has certainly helped – as soon as he gets put into his cot at night, he 'knows' it's sleepy time.

Katie from Tunbridge Wells, mum to Dylan, four months

I can't understand why sleeping through the night is constantly touted as an ideal to be reached as soon as possible. Very few of the mums I know have been lucky enough to have babies who magically started sleeping through when they were 'supposed' to. I know it's largely a cultural thing, as we in the west seem so keen to get our children to be as independent as soon as possible. My son started to sleep for about seven or eight hours a night at three months (having been waking two or three times a night for breastfeeding, which never troubled me). Then he started teething and his sleep pattern got 'worse' rather than better.

I was getting up so often to breastfeed and comfort him that we decided to co-sleep, as that made life easier for all of us. But those hard times, they don't last. I think there's a lot of fear that if we don't get babies to do something by a certain time, then they 'never' will. But of course they do. They learn to crawl and walk and talk when they are ready, and the same goes for sleeping through.

Tammy from Walthamstow, mum to Jake, one

The all-important bedtime routine

All the experts agree that a consistent, regular bedtime routine is the most important factor in paving the way to peaceful evenings and undisturbed nights. If you provide your baby with a series of sleep 'cues' or 'associations' (in other words, whatever it is that he comes to recognise as a signal that it's time to go to sleep) and repeat the process at the same time every evening, making it as pleasant an experience as possible, he will soon start to see this bedtime routine as the precursor to sleep.

Anything from six to eight weeks is a good time to start a bedtime routine, as it's then that your baby starts to become more aware of the difference between day and night, and is more responsive to the cues you set up.

What should a bedtime routine involve?

It doesn't matter too much *what* you do – the important thing is doing the same thing every night, at the same time, with all the different elements carried out in the same order. Your aim is to be really consistent – initially, at least – with the obvious drawback that this can become a bit tedious for you and doesn't allow for much flexibility at that time of the evening. (You may, for instance, have to get into the habit of recording your favourite soap, if it happens to coincide with the all-important bedtime window.) However, most parents feel these drawbacks are a price worth paying.

For many babies, a bedtime routine starts with a warm bath. If you do give your baby a bath, though, make it short and calming, rather than noisy and fun. You might want to try a spot of baby massage before putting on a sleep suit, giving him a feed and a cuddle, then reading him a story or singing a song. (It's never too early to begin reading to your baby and a favourite book, read last thing, can become a reliable bedtime sleep cue.) If he has a comforter (see page 50), handing it to him at the last minute before bed can have the same effect. And some parents find that using the same few, comforting words or sounds will also do the job – for instance, 'Shhh. Goodnight now.'

Keep the lights dim and your voice low while you are doing all this, to help him understand it's night-time, not daytime. Then put him in his cot, say goodnight and leave the room. It's important to put him down awake so he can settle himself independently: this is also a much-recommended piece of advice from the sleep experts, and it's discussed in more detail below.

Make it happy

Aim to get the atmosphere and environment right during your bedtime routine. Do the pre-amble in the room he's going to sleep in and make sure it's warm, dimly lit and quiet. Remember, it should be a quiet, calming-down experience – so definitely not the moment for a boisterous chuck-around with Dad. And, above all, it should be enjoyable: your aim is to make your baby come to see going to bed as a positive thing. And, if he's comfortable and happy in the environment he drops off in, he's more likely to be happy to stay there when he wakes up subsequently in the night.

Don't forget that your frame of mind could affect proceedings, too. If your baby senses you're stressed or unhappy, it could rub off on him. So if you're having a bad evening and your partner's not around to take over, take a few moments pre-bedtime to chill out with the help of some deep breathing and, if necessary, a glass of wine, a cup of tea, or a bar of chocolate.

When should bedtime be?

It depends when your baby starts to become sleepy and ready for bed but, typically, it will be somewhere between 6pm and 8pm. What's key is making sure you get the right window. There's no point trying to put him down if he's not tired (or likely to be at some point within the next half an hour) and, equally, if you miss the all-important 'sleep window' and he becomes overtired, he'll be crabby and too tired to settle. So when you're establishing a bedtime, look for the usual early signals that your baby is starting to get tired – perhaps he sucks his thumb, rubs his ears or grizzles – and grab the moment. After a little while – assuming his waking and daytime nap schedule has a fairly regular pattern to it – you'll find he becomes tired and ready for bed at the same time every night, so you won't have to wait to see the signals, you can simply go by the clock.

As a general rule, about half an hour is a good time to allow for the pre-bedtime routine. Any less and you'll be too rushed to fit everything in; any more and he may end up too tired to settle – plus, it will eat into your evening. But, however long bedtime is, try to remain business-like about winding it up. Read the book, sing the song, say goodnight and leave without lingering. If your baby senses he could have your company for a while longer, he may try to exploit it!

And don't forget that, while it's a good idea to be very consistent at first and to keep to your routine as far as possible, you'll find that there is room to be flexible once it's well established. Inevitably there'll be times when bedtime goes out the window – the odd special occasion; holidays; or other times when something unscheduled and unavoidable upends your usual routine. But if you've made bedtime a firmly entrenched habit at home, you should find you've got scope to deviate from it sometimes without the whole process going pear shaped.

Louise says: If you've worked hard to get a bedtime routine in place, it's easy to become a bit obsessed about keeping it that way. But the good news is that, once it becomes par-for-the-course for your baby, there's almost always room for manoeuvre. Mums in particular can get a little over-anxious about deviation from the norm, largely because we're the ones who have to deal with any problems. But my advice is to take a deep breath and try being flexible sometimes. Often a change of environment makes little difference – if you're away, or staying with friends, just do the same things you usually do, at the same sort of time. The change in surroundings is unlikely to throw them much. And do take that evening out if the chance arises! Your other half, or any other willing babysitter that your baby's familiar with, can no doubt do the bedtime routine just as well as you . . .

What the netmums say

We love bedtime routines!

I'm dead set on bedtime routines. My son has had the same routine since he was three months old, although we've gradually made bedtime later, the older he's got. He goes to bed straight away with no problems, has never once asked to stay up late or refused to go to bed. Because we started his routine young, he's not aware of any other options! I enjoy having the time to myself.

Jill from Whitchurch, mum to Alex, four

I instituted a bedtime routine almost immediately with both of my children. It always started with a bath, then a massage with baby lotion, then into their nightwear. They'd then be breastfed, winded and taken to their cot while still awake. We'd settle them into their cot quickly, then leave the room, turn off the light and turn on some gentle classical music on the way out. In the early days, we'd hear a few whimpers and have to go back in and comfort them. But, sure enough, by about four weeks, they could both fall asleep on their own. And as they became more practised at it, they gradually slept for longer and longer. I'm convinced it's helped them get through problems like teething and fighting illness, and has generally just been very good for them, as well as for my husband and I! And it's changed very little over the years. Breastfeeding has been replaced by a cup of warm milk, and there's now a story, too, before heading to the bathroom before the bedroom. But it's still a case of a quick goodnight, music on, light off = two happy children and two happy parents!

Sandra from Berkhamsted, mum to Gemma, six, and David, four

Our son's bedtime routine began at eight weeks and he started sleeping through a week later. Daddy has always been in charge of bedtimes – a great bonding time for him and a rest for me! Food, bath, milk, bed. Once in bed, the light stays off and we don't take him out of the cot or out of his room unless really necessary. If he cries we take it in turns to go in to him every ten minutes, just to reassure him then leave right away. We stuck to the routine like glue for the first couple of months and then noticed that we dreaded the idea of not being able to give him a bath for fear that he might not settle. We realised we needed to loosen up a bit and started by not giving him a bath one evening a week . . . which led to two . . . and now he just has baths two or three times a week. I think it's the parents' energy and atmosphere of the house at bedtime that makes all the difference. We try to stay relaxed, keep the telly off until he's gone down, and not let him know he's missing out on exciting things when he's in bed. It's worked so far!

Gemma from Radlett, mum to Callum, one

A routine is crucial if you want a happy baby! Putting them down at the same time each night is important, but it's equally important not to let them sleep in. I wake our kids each morning at 7am. That way they then go down for their daytime naps at the same time each day, too. It means you (and they) know exactly where you are, which means happy babies and happy mummy! People often comment on how content my kids are and I put it 100% down to being in a routine early on.

Sam from Basingstoke, mum to Jacob, two, and Evie, one

The art of self-settling

One of the best steps you can take towards getting a good night's sleep is teaching or encouraging your baby to 'self-settle'. If your baby can get to sleep by himself when you put him down for the evening (and for daytime naps, see below), then he won't need you – or any other sleep cue that you have to get up for in order to provide, such as a feed or a cuddle – to drop off again.

So, if you haven't done already, it's a great idea to start putting your baby down while he's still awake (although he should be sleepy – if he's wide awake he's unlikely to drop off without a fuss!). If you've rocked, fed or cuddled him to sleep until now, he may well object to this change in the system. But be persistent. The earlier you can get this cracked, the easier it is to do so.

If it's a feed that's become your baby's sleep cue, you can alter this by giving it earlier in the bedtime routine – perhaps before his story or song, before you put his pyjamas on, or even right at the start, before his bath. Or, if you prefer to keep it the last thing and he does drop off while feeding, you could try rousing him gently so he's awake when you put him in his cot.

Of course, there's something lovely about a baby dropping off in your arms and some parents are reluctant to let that go (many babies aren't that keen to ditch it, either). So, don't feel you have to stop doing it if you're enjoying it. Just be aware that you're setting up a pattern which will be harder to crack the longer it goes on for. One day, you might just be keen to get your evenings back, and be less inclined to cuddle, rock or feed in the dead of night.

What the netmums say

Self-settling and good/bad sleep associations

Sleep has always been an issue in our house. When our first daughter came along we spent many nights bouncing, rocking and swaying her to sleep – the poor thing probably couldn't go to sleep because she had motion sickness! My husband would drive her up and down the A13 to get her to

sleep and then roll her out of her car seat into the cot. Now, at seven, she still wakes in the night for a cuddle. Our second daughter was also a poor sleeper – she slept with us and I don't remember her ever sleeping in her own bed all night before the age of two. We finally took her to a sleep clinic because I was so exhausted and grumpy. Thankfully our third slept all night long from about ten weeks. What a Godsend.
Katie from South Woodham Ferrers, mum to Abi, seven, Lucy, five, and Evie, two

We had a terrible time with our eldest when it came to sleeping. He was small, fed frequently and was difficult to settle. But he was our first born, so we did what was easiest, so we could all get sleep. He'd only settle in his cot after falling asleep in our arms and, a lot of the time, he ended up in our bed anyway. This got worse and, as a toddler, he would never settle in his room. Finally, when he was about five, he outgrew it. Meanwhile, we had our second child and decided to be strong from the beginning, putting him into a cot and leaving him to settle himself. He slept through at two months and has never come into our bed and never wanted to. When our little girl was born we got her in a good bedtime routine from a few weeks old and always placed her in her cot awake with her Taggie blanket. She, too, sleeps well all night and is a very happy toddler.
Helen from Aberdeen, mum to Jack, nine, James, eight, and Freya, one

We sing a couple of songs last thing and we always finish off with 'Twinkle, Twinkle, Little Star', before the light goes off and the nightlight goes on. My daughter's had the same routine since she was six months old, and I don't think it's an exaggeration to say that it saved my sanity. She's generally always settled by 8pm.

Angie from Arlesey, mum to Freya, five

I blame myself for a lot of my daughter's sleep habits. When we had her we lived in a flat and I was always conscious of her waking the neighbours, so wouldn't let her cry. I always used milk to get her to sleep so, even now, if she's upset, her comfort is milk in a bottle. I always went to her if she cried or even murmured. At three, she now has her own double bed, and I have to lie with her till she's asleep then sneak out, which means when she wakes in the night (on a good night, once; a lot of the time, twice or three times) she wonders where I am and either cries for me or comes to get me. So, I have made 'a rod for my own back', as my mum and mother-in-law would say! I find that my daughter can sometimes be grouchy as she's obviously tired and consequently I am too. I love her dearly and wouldn't swap her for anything but sometimes I wonder when those blissful uninterrupted nights are going to start.

Nova from Manchester, mum to Poppy, three

Fae was not a great sleeper and was 18 months before she slept through a full night without any waking. We realised when she was three months old that we were the problem rather than Fae, as we hadn't got a routine and had got into bad habits (her sleeping on our shoulders while we watched TV, for example). As soon as we instigated a daily routine she was more settled and slept better. She was (and still is) asleep by 6.45pm every night and generally sleeps until about midnight, then would wake two or three times. We persisted with our routine and when she woke would comfort her but try not to interact with her, and she seemed to get the message that waking up was boring and she'd be better off asleep.

Suzanne from St Helens, mum to Fae, three, and Connor, ten months

We used to read my eldest daughter a book at bedtime called *Pyjamas*, about a little girl who's going to bed. At the end, the girl in the book settles down and goes off to sleep. Nina got into the habit of kissing her goodnight, and so that was always the moment when she knew she was heading for her cot. It was a perfect sleep cue. We did it for several years – although, for some reason, my younger daughter never took to the book in the same way. She preferred *Each, Peach, Pear, Plum!*

Julia from Milton Keynes, mum to Nina, five, and Ellie, three

When Freya was newborn, she would fall asleep on the breast or bottle, and then go into her cot asleep; or else I would rock her to sleep. This was fine to begin with, but she's a light sleeper, so would wake when placed in the cot and, as she got bigger, all that rocking got very tiring! One night when she was six months old, at about 3am, I just couldn't do it. I was exhausted, my partner was snoring away oblivious and I just knew that if I didn't lie down, I would fall down. So I laid Freya down in her cot, made sure she was warm and comfy, and went back to my bed. She cried for maybe two minutes, then settled herself to sleep – it was a revelation to me. I didn't know she could do it. From there on in, I never rocked her to sleep again. I simply put her in her cot after her bottle and story, sang to her for a couple of minutes and quietly left the room. It didn't work perfectly every time and, if she cried for more than a couple of minutes, I would go back in and

reassure her, never lifting her out of the cot. If I have another child, I'll try to teach them to self-settle sooner!
Angie from Arlesey, mum to Freya, five

Reducing night-time feeds

Once your baby is three months old you can take steps towards decreasing the amount of feeding he's doing at night, if he's still waking up more than a couple of times for milk, and earn yourself some longer chunks of sleep as a result. Although it's too early to cut out night feeds entirely, a healthy three-month-old who is feeding well in the day shouldn't need more than one or two feeds (or even, possibly, three) at night (ie, from an early bedtime through to a reasonable time of the morning). So if yours is still demanding more than that, you can cut back by gradually widening the space in between feeds by short periods, perhaps of 15 minutes. So, instead of feeding your baby immediately when he wakes, you make him wait for a little while, giving a pat or a stroke instead, or maybe by allowing him to suck on a dummy or your finger. Although it's true that this might amount to swapping one 'undesirable' sleep association for another, it's better to break the feed/sleep association first, if you can. If your baby comes to realise that all he'll get for his efforts is a quick suck or a stroke rather than the feed he was hoping for, he's very likely to roll over and go to sleep again. (And don't forget, it's always a good idea to wait a while once you've heard your baby wake in the night. Try giving him a few moments to settle on his own and return to sleep without you – you may find he surprises you by doing so.)

Once he *has* relinquished a certain regular night feed for a couple of nights in succession, you can be sure he doesn't need that feed any more. So, even if he does take to waking again at that point, don't be tempted to give him a feed. Offer a comforter, a soothing stroke, or a bottle of water, instead.

Keep repeating the same 'spacing' process and after a couple of nights when your baby's adjusted, you can try extending the gap between feeds by a further 15 minutes and so on, until you've created longer and longer gaps in between.

Gradual spacing of feeds is the only kind way to cut them out at this stage. You can wait and go for a more drastic 'cold turkey' approach, if you prefer, cutting them all out in one go. But you can only do this once your baby is six months old, when you can do so in conjunction with some form of sleep training. There's more on that in the following chapter.

Don't forget to keep night feeds dark, quiet and 'business-like'. Unless he has a dirty nappy, you can probably get away without changing your baby's nappy at night now, which means you can get him back into bed with even less disturbance after a feed.

Dream feeding

Some parents find it suits them well to wake their baby up at around 10 or 11pm, just before they head for bed themselves, and offer a feed to prolong the next stretch of sleep further than it would go otherwise. Most then find that, at some point, they can simply drop this feed and their little one slumbers on. There's no harm in using this method if you find it does indeed give you a significant amount of extra sleep – although many professionals remain convinced it's better never to wake a sleeping baby!

Maggie says: Although tempting, I'd advise against waking a sleeping baby for a 'dream feed', as it can interfere with their natural sleep/wake rhythm. Often it's not that helpful as a baby will wake at the same time he or she would have done anyway, without the dream feed. And, as time goes on, he *will* sleep for longer periods quite naturally.

Will a bottle of formula help?

If you've been exclusively breastfeeding so far, you might wonder if a bottle of formula given as a last thing could help your baby sleep a little longer at night. Some mums find this to be the case, since formula milk isn't so easily digested as breastmilk and is likely to leave a baby fuller for longer. The other advantage is that your other half can give the last feed, allowing you to get an early night – or maybe even have an evening out. If you do go for this option, though, bear in mind that your breasts will quickly adapt to the new routine and produce less milk accordingly. So, once you've definitely cut this last feed out, you won't easily be able to reinstate it should you want to.

Never be tempted to put extra formula, cereal, or anything else in a baby's bottle to thicken it, or, for that matter, consider introducing solids before the time's right, in the hope of a better night's sleep. Babies' stomachs just aren't ready for solids of any kind before four months (17 weeks) at the earliest and, in fact, six months is the recommended start point for weaning. Putting anything other than the proper quantity of formula milk in the bottle could put him at risk of choking, dehydration, constipation and even – later in life – obesity.

Maggie says: I'd issue one word of caution if you've been exclusively breastfeeding and you do decide to try formula as a last feed, in search of a much-needed night's sleep.

Pro-breastfeeding groups point out that if you introduce formula for one feed or more you run the risk of reducing your prolactin levels, which are higher at night. Prolactin is a hormone that stimulates your milk production and, if these drop, it can affect your milk supply in the day. Added to that, recent research has highlighted the beneficial effects of breastfeeding at night-time, since naturally occurring chemicals that are linked to sleepiness – called nucleotides – only reach their highest concentration in breastmilk that's produced at night. Of course, as with so many things, there's a balance to be struck between your needs for rest and sleep, and the needs of your little one. After all, a rested mum is likely to be happier than a tired one, and a happier mum is likely to have a happier baby.

What the netmums say

Last feeds and night feeds

A real turning point came at around four months, when we introduced a bottle of formula after her bath, followed by a proper bedtime routine. I woke her when I went to bed around half ten, changed her nappy and gave her a breastfeed top up. From this time on, she slept really well until about 7am most days. About two months later, I dropped the late feed and she didn't seem to mind, carrying on sleeping through until 7ish. Looking back, I think we could have introduced more structure to her bedtime a bit earlier, but we were a bit naive, it being our first baby! But, also, I think we were lucky to be blessed with a baby who loves her sleep.

Cath from Bristol, mum to Carmella, two

Joe needed to breastfeed every three hours in the early weeks, and sometimes even more frequently between 11pm and 3am. We managed to overcome this by giving a formula dream feed at 11pm, which seemed to settle him and allowed me a break from breastfeeding. I tried to let him feed as much as he wanted in the day so he would be fuller for the night-time, and after three months the night feeds gradually got further apart, until the 3am feed became 6am. When he was six months, we were going abroad and had to be up at 2am, so we didn't give the 11pm dream feed. He didn't ask for it and from that day on he didn't require a night feed at all! There are so many theories, tips and tricks about babies and sleep. My advice would be to be open-minded, and try what feels right for you and your baby. Nothing is set in stone and every baby and parent differ from the next, so what works for one family may not work for another. It's hard, but it does get easier.

Emma from Chester, mum to Joseph, ten months

My son slept through the night from ten weeks. I was breastfeeding and found it worked well to 'cluster feed' [see page 54] him towards the end of the day before putting him to bed for the night. So, in the day he went for three hours in between feeds but, a few hours before bedtime, I'd feed him every one or two hours, and I'm sure this helped him to go longer at night between feeds.

Eleanor from Inverness, mum to Callum, one

When Madison was born we spent two nights in hospital where I was made to wake her up every two hours for a feed – because of this, she woke every two hours for about three weeks. Then, all of a sudden, on Saturday night she slept from

1.30am until 7.30am – we had such a shock and had to make sure she was ok! I was giving her a dream feed at about midnight and I found that she was going through till about 4am. She cluster feeds in the evening between 8am and 11pm which means that it is unlikely that we get to bed before midnight. But she does sleep till 9am now!

Rachel from Stafford, mum to Madison, three months

I think I had the exception to the rule when it came to sleep and feeding. From the age of six to eight weeks my daughter was the most determined sleeper. She would sleep from 5.30 pm until 6am. I offered her dream feeds at around 11pm each night, but she rarely took any milk – I'd have to sit with her for half an hour with the bottle at her lips before she'd even let it into her mouth and then I could be waiting another ten minutes for her to suck, if at all. Often she would wake up properly just long enough to turn her head away and then go back to sleep. Looking back I wish I'd just let her dictate when she wanted the milk rather than disturbing her sleep (and mine) by trying to feed her at 11pm, whether she wanted it or not!

Caroline from Wakefield, mum to Jessica, one

Harry used to wake every two hours and eventually got himself into a three-hour pattern around nine or ten weeks. By 11 weeks we noticed he wasn't taking much of his last bottle feed at 10pm and, as we'd introduced the bath-bottle-bed routine by then, we thought we'd see how things went if we just dropped it. He hasn't woken in the night for a feed since – except on one occasion when he had teething troubles.

Angela from Liverpool, mum to Harry, six months

Daytime sleep

Because they need so much sleep for their health and development, babies and toddlers need to sleep a certain amount in the day, too, in order to get their full quota. Naps are vital if a little one is to make it through the day without becoming irritable – as any parent will tell you. And getting the right amount of sleep, at the right sort of time during the day, will help your baby to sleep better generally, because overtired babies can be stressed and fidgety, and resistant to settling. On top of all that, having a routine or regular schedule for naps (and for feeds, too) will help you establish and maintain a bedtime, because if your baby becomes used to sleeping at certain times in the day, he'll always be ready to sleep at a certain time of the evening, too.

Although daytime naps, like feeding, may be all over the place in the early weeks, your baby will naturally begin to settle into a more predictable schedule after a month or two and you may be able to capitalise on this by aiming to put him down for naps at the same sort of time each day. It will help if feeds take place at routine times, too – again, a pattern will establish itself naturally, but you can encourage one to take shape by aiming to be consistent when you offer the bottle or breast.

On the other hand, not all babies are born 'good nappers'. Some need a bit of help on their way to being one. Others develop good napping habits, quite naturally, with time.

How much naptime should my baby have?

Like night-time sleep habits, patterns of daytime napping are extremely variable – some babies can be zonked out for several hours, several times a day, while others can get by on one kip a day, or are content to snatch a frequent 20 minutes here and there. It probably doesn't matter that much – although you're likely to know about it if your baby *isn't* napping enough during the day, because she'll be thoroughly grumpy. Equally, it's possible for a baby to nap too much in the day at the expense of night-time sleep and, if that happens, you may have to take some gradual steps to redress the balance. The chart below gives an idea of what's average but, don't forget, there's very wide variation.

How often and for how long your baby naps is a pattern that will change quite a bit over the course of their first three years. Most parents find it's a natural process and that it's quite easy to adapt when changes arise. Your baby will let you know when he's ready to 'drop' one of his naps, because he simply won't seem tired at the same time any more, and the remaining naps or nap will shift forwards or backwards accordingly. It may take a little time for him to settle into a changed nap routine but, more than likely, it will be in place within a few weeks.

Louise says: Generally speaking, it's not a good idea to let a baby nap after 4pm, if you want them to be tired and ready to settle at a reasonable bedtime. So, although it's usually better *not* to wake a sleeping baby, I would do so if they are sleeping past this time – particularly if you're trying to establish a bedtime routine, or are in the middle of a sleep-training programme. Of course, you may have to take other factors into account. If you're in the car on a long journey, there won't be a great deal you can do about it, except wake them when you get home!

What's normal for napping?

- As a newborn, your baby is likely to nap very frequently, for several hours at a time.
- By around three months, your baby's naps are likely to have

settled into some kind of pattern. He'll probably nap three times day (perhaps four), typically including one in the morning, a couple of hours after waking, one in the middle of the day, and one in the afternoon.

- At six months, your baby is likely to be down to two or perhaps three naps a day; typically a morning and an afternoon nap; or two shorter naps morning and afternoon, with a longer one in the middle of the day.

- At 12 months plus, your baby is likely to go down to one nap daily; typically one to two hours in the middle of the day. He'll probably give up naps altogether at some point between the ages of two and five.

When and where should naps be?

Generally speaking, your baby will let you know when he's getting tired and in need of a nap. Be on the alert for signs from your baby – yawning, rubbing of ears or eyes, and crabbiness are the most common – and put him down as soon as the window arises. If you miss it, he may not want to sleep at all and then you'll have a cranky baby on your hands who will probably drop off much later, instead, and then be too lively to go to bed at the right time.

There are two schools of thought about where to put your baby for his nap. Some say he'll always get a good, deep, uninterrupted kip if you make sure he goes into his cot, which – assuming you've got bedtime sussed – he'll associate with sleeping and where he will be most comfortable. Others say it's better to be very flexible about nap-times and encourage your baby to sleep on the go, whether it be in a car seat, carrycot or pram, so that you can fit travel, trips and the rest of your life around his napping needs.

There's no real right and wrong here – which way you go will probably depend on your lifestyle. In particular, whether you have other children or not will certainly be influential (for more on coping with siblings and sleep issues, see page 150). But it's a good idea to steer clear of a situation where he's dependent on one specific environment in order to fall asleep during the day, and to aim for a baby who's able to nap well wherever he is. A good rule of thumb is to make sure he always has at least one of his daytime naps in his cot – then it won't matter much if the others are taken on the hoof.

Maggie says: After lunch is a good natural point for a child of any age to nap. There's a good reason why Europeans have what they call 'siesta time' – it's when our body clock winds down, which it does twice a day, once in the early afternoon, after lunch, and again at 3am. So it's a really good time to encourage your baby to have a daytime sleep, as you have nature on your side. And it's usually the best time slot to stick to once your baby is down to one nap a day.

Safe napping

For safety's sake, the Foundation for the Study of Infant Death Syndrome (FSID) recommends that, as with night-time sleep, you put your baby down for naps in the same room as you until he is six months old. This is fine if he's in a portable Moses basket or a bouncy chair, but not too practical once he's outgrown those options. A good compromise would be to potter around not too far from your baby and to make very regular checks on him, as he snoozes.

If your baby is napping in his car seat, be sure to bring the seat into the house first, remove hats and outer clothing if he's likely to get too hot, check him regularly and make sure he's not napping in a car seat for more than a couple of hours, to avoid putting a strain on his spine.

How can I get my baby to nap?

If your baby won't nap, or doesn't seem to nap for long enough, you could try:

- Establishing a pre-nap routine. Use a modified, rather than a full-on, version of your bedtime routine, spending perhaps ten minutes before nap-time in the room where he'll be sleeping quietly winding down. Use any positive sleep cues he's used to at night, such as a favourite song or book. If he has a comforter, make sure that's close by.

- Making sure all the conditions are right for sleeping: is he the right temperature; comfortable; recently fed; wearing a clean, dry nappy? Is it reasonably peaceful? (Although it's always good for a baby to get used to sleeping among a certain amount of background noise.) It might also help to draw the curtains, but better if it's not totally dark, to avoid him getting confused between day and night.

- Encouraging your baby to self-settle for nap-times, just the same as at bedtime, by making sure he's awake when you put him down to sleep. If he can self-settle, he's more likely to go back to sleep if he wakes up mid-nap before he's really ready.

- Not jumping up to go to him if he wakes from a nap after a short time: leave him alone for a while to see if he drops off again. A stroke or a few quiet words of comfort from you may aid this.

- Getting the 'sleep window' right. Timing is everything! Put your baby down as soon as you can see he's starting to get sleepy (don't even hang around with the pre-nap routine stuff). If he's not yet tired, or he's past tired and on to a second wind, he's likely to object.

- Trying to structure your day so his naps occur at similar times. So much the better if his naps always come after certain other elements of his routine – a feed, for example. Have a regular bedtime routine and try to offer feeds at set times, too. If the rest of his 24 hours follows a pattern, his daytime kips are likely to, too.

- Taking him for a long walk in the pram or sling, or putting him in the car seat and taking him for a drive. Most parents find this is a fail-safe way to get their baby to nap, but be warned: you don't want it to become the only way he'll go to sleep in the day because it will become a horrible drag for you. So keep on putting him in the cot sometimes, too. Persistence – along with some of the tips above – is likely to pay off.

- If your baby is six months or more, the sleep-training techniques outlined in the following chapter can be used at nap-times, too.

What the netmums say

Naps

All of my children have been 'trained' to take their naps in their cot (or bed, as they got older). It means I can guarantee the youngest will always go down for a good sleep in the afternoon – and the other two were the same. However, it can be a tie if we want to go out anywhere as she will only

sleep for 20 minutes max in the buggy or car. (And yes, the other two were the same!)
Zoe from Bristol, mum to Rubi, six, Raegan, three, and Minnie, one

Sam went from four naps a day down to three at around five months. He cut the afternoon one out at about eight months, then he cut the morning sleep at ten months and, from then onwards, has just slept at lunchtime for one to two hours. It was easy to know when he was ready to drop a nap, as he simply refused to go to sleep. I always try to be home for his lunchtime nap, as he sleeps better in the cot – although he's OK in the car seat or buggy sometimes, he wakes sooner.
Isobel from London, mum to Sam, one

We've had an awful first year of night-time sleeping and I've just come to terms with the fact that I don't get to sleep much any more. I do find her naps are really important, in terms of her being better at night. If she's had a busy day and has not had her usual naps (usually one in the morning for about half an hour and one in the afternoon for about an hour, although sometimes more, sometimes less) she's a nightmare all night! She definitely sleeps best at night when she's had her naps.
Shelley from Taunton, mum to Atiya, one

My oldest daughter would only nap in the car. Consequently I spent several hours a day (and heaven knows how much money on petrol) driving round while she slept! I've no idea, looking back, how I managed to get into that situation. Needless to say, my second daughter was a lot more flexible – I made sure of it.
Julia from Milton Keynes, mum to Nina, five, and Ellie, three

I found napping so important – but it took me a long time to work it out. Good naps definitely equal a happy baby; and a baby who is more willing to go to bed at night, and then sleep through. Thomas sleeps best in his cot and I try to plan my day so that I can have him napping there – I've been known not to attend things so he doesn't miss out! But I'd much prefer that than not getting any sleep at night. He has two naps a day and sleeps about two and a half to three hours in total. And I never wake him from a nap unless it gets too close to bedtime. Three hours before is our limit.

Nikki from Hertford, mum to Thomas, eight months

My daughter has always been a terrible daytime sleeper, yet slept (and still does) really well at night-time. I've tried the tips in almost every book to get her to have consistent naps during the day, yet I've failed to find any that have worked for me. I try to put her down at the same time, morning and afternoon. Sometimes she sleeps for 20 minutes, sometimes for almost three hours. Sometimes not at all. But regardless, her night-time sleeping is (bar the odd illness or teething bout) almost identical. She goes down between 6.30pm and 7pm, and sleeps through soundly until about 6.30am, regardless of the number or length of naps she's had. To be honest, I found the whole nap thing very stressful at first as she would be totally exhausted in the day, yet still not sleep. Now, I've come to the conclusion that if she sleeps, great. If not, then we'll muddle through.

Lesley from London, mum to Imogen, ten months

I've always put my daughter to sleep in her pram outside during the day (well wrapped up in winter, of course). The benefit of this is you can get them to sleep wherever you are, whether visiting friends, on holiday, or out for the day. Wherever we are, my daughter always has her sleep at the usual time, and wakes up refreshed and able to enjoy the afternoon out – unlike some of our friends' babies who won't sleep in their prams and then get cranky. If you get them into this sort of habit at an early age it means you can continue with them even when the child is older and potentially more difficult to settle.

Jenny from London, mum to Jessica, four, and Poppy, one

I never had a problem with nap routines; I really just let the children make their own. I think all children will nap when they need to eventually. Mollie has three a day, but they're quite short now, 25–40 minutes. She naps in her baby chair downstairs, regardless of any noise around her. My sons still nap, too, at the same time every day. They settle down on the sofa with their blankets and sleep for usually an hour at least. We used to put them in their cots to nap, but none of them would sleep well there. I think it's a comfort thing – they like to hear us and know they're not alone as they fall asleep. Naps are certainly a must for my children, their moods and energy levels are improved, and as long as they have plenty to do in the day, it doesn't affect their sleep. Although, I do find with Oliver that if he naps later in the day and we've not had an active day his bedtime can end up very late.

Katherine from Cambridge, mum to Ethan, three, Oliver, two, and Mollie, nine months

Should I wake my baby in the morning?

Once your baby has a fairly good daytime nap schedule and a regular evening routine, it's pretty unlikely you'll need to wake him in the morning anyway, since babies who've gone to bed at a reasonable hour are very likely to wake early, too (and, for many parents, much earlier than is desirable – see below). However, if your baby has a tendency to snooze late in the morning and you're keen to get a tighter schedule up and running, or you're planning to undertake sleep training [see page 103] and you need to be certain he'll be tired enough by the end of the day, it's probably a good idea to wake him if he looks like slumbering past 7am or so.

Maggie says: Generally, it's better to let a natural sleep/wake rhythm evolve if you can. But it's true that if a baby wakes late it can have an impact on the rest of the day, and his needs must fit in with your life, so there may be a compromise to be reached. I would say wake them up if you want to get them into a proper routine and be in sync with the rest of the household. But, if it suits you to let them sleep late and you can get a lie-in as well, then go for it. It's all about what suits you and your baby.

Louise says: It's a good idea to take an 'up-and-at-'em' approach when your baby wakes in the morning, certainly if you're sleep training or trying to establish a schedule. Giving structure to the day early on can be helpful in keeping the rest of the day's routines running smoothly, and also helps to make the change between day and night clearer for your little one. If he's awake and ready for the day at around 7am, say, he'll probably be ready to sleep for his nap at suitable times and, likewise, when it comes round, for bedtime.

Early risers

Most parents of young babies have to accept that the day begins a lot earlier than it used to – especially if it's a direct payoff for a nice, early bedtime and the evening to yourself. Fact is, babies tend to wake early – and it's hardly unreasonable if they've been put to bed early the night before. However, if your baby wakes wanting to start the day at something truly ungodly, you might want to look for ways to push his waking time back, if possible. Obviously, what constitutes ungodly is a personal thing, but for many parents 6am is just about acceptable. Anything before about 5am is *definitely* not daytime and should be considered a night waking which, after six months, you can justifiably tackle with sleep training (see page 103).

Solutions for early risers

- Double-check that there's nothing waking him such as a noisy milkman, or the heating coming on.
- Try thicker or blackout blinds. (Lots of parents find these do get them a bit of extra shut-eye but the drawback is that you create an artificially dark environment and you'll need them wherever you are, and at any time of year. Some say it is far better to forgo them and get your baby used to falling asleep in lighter conditions, too, which will make them more flexible.)
- For older babies and toddlers, you can buy a special alarm clock (most of these seem to feature a rabbit with ears that pop up at the time you've set it for), or set up a lamp attached to a timer. Then you let them know that they cannot get up (if they're in a bed, you may also need a stairgate across the door if this is going to work) until the ears go up, or the light goes on. You can then bring the time back gradually.

- Put off attending to your baby for as long as possible when he wakes. He might well be happy to amuse himself for a while, especially if you put a few age-appropriate toys in his cot the night before, and leave a non-spill beaker of water nearby so he can quench his thirst if necessary. You never know – he *just* might drop off again.

- Try giving him a later bedtime to see if you get a correspondingly later rising time. The main problem with this is that you don't get an evening to yourself (and that's a compromise you may not be willing to make!). However – and this is the other problem – there's no guarantee it will actually have the desired effect. Lots of parents find that it doesn't matter *when* their baby is put to bed . . . they still wake early in the morning!

- If you're forced to get up earlier than you can bear to take a bright-eyed, bushy-tailed baby downstairs for the start of his day, don't be ashamed to put the television on if it will keep him distracted for a useful period of time – you might have to be up and awake with your baby while the rest of the world slumbers . . . but actually entertaining him may be above and beyond the call of duty!

- Be philosophical. Accept that as a parent your day is likely to start earlier than it used to and, for many, it's a worthy payoff if their baby is settled in bed at a reasonable hour, giving them peaceful evenings. Babies tend to outgrow early mornings in the same way that they – eventually – outgrow night wakings. So it might help to remember that he *will* begin to give you more of a lie-in at some point – and that you'll get your revenge when he's a teenager and you can wake *him* up well before he'd like you to.

What the netmums say

Early risers

My first born was an early riser. Putting him back to bed just didn't work; he liked to come in our room, so I kept a box of quiet toys and books to entertain him until we got up at a reasonable time. Now he has a very dark room and toys in there and he stays put for a while – but he's a better sleeper in general, now, anyway. My second son has started waking early, too. The cot mobile we have is a godsend – it projects fish on the ceiling and plays classical music. He loves it and because it comes with a remote, we don't have to hover over the cot winding it up; I can switch it on while I'm still half asleep. I'm not a morning person!
Steph from Camborne, mum to Jamie, three, and Oscar, five months

My eldest son went through a stage of waking early. He'd often call us at 5am and I was unsure what to do. At first I tried explaining to him that he needed to sleep a little longer but, unfortunately, it didn't make a difference. After weeks of waking up early I decided I had had enough and I just ignored his calling. He wasn't in distress or crying so I figured it wasn't going to harm him. After a couple of days he stopped waking at 5am and slept till 6.30 or 7am. I feel a lot more refreshed now!
Irma from Oldham, mum to Damir, two, and Aydin, eight months

When Harry was almost two he started to wake very early so we used a nightlight attached to a timer plug to come on at a reasonable time in the morning. This let him know he was

allowed to get out of bed and play with his toys. If the light wasn't on he had to stay in bed. It worked really well.
Sam from Harlow, mum to Harry, two

Do I really have to bother with all this routine business?

No, it's not compulsory! Some parents like to spend the evenings cuddling or playing with their babies (especially if one or both are working during the day and it's the only chance you get). And if you're bedsharing, you will have to, for safety's sake, take your baby to bed when you go yourselves (unless he starts his evening off in a cot and moves in with you a bit later). It may also suit you better to let your baby snooze late into the morning and wake up naturally. And many parents prefer to take a flexible approach to naps so they can fit the rest of their lives around them during the day.

You can always introduce a regular bedtime at a later stage if you want – it's just that, as a general rule, the longer you stick with this kind of habit, the more entrenched it becomes and the harder it will be to change once you decide you want to. But that's up to you!

What the netmums say

Routines are not compulsory!

The only consistent things in both my kids' routines are the fact that they have pyjamas on. Sometimes they have baths, sometimes they don't, mostly they're in bed for 7.30pm, sometimes it's 7pm, sometimes it can even be 9pm, if we've been busy and they've had extra naps during the day because we've been out in the car. They sleep fine!

Danni from Doncaster, mum to Emily, two, and Robert, seven months

We don't really have much of a routine. I try to get both of my children in bed between 7pm and 8pm and that's about it. Sometimes we read a story, sometimes we don't. Sometimes we have a bath before bed; other times I give them a bath before dinner. I'm a very flexible person myself and I just struggle to stick to routines and clock-watching!

Irma from Oldham, mum to Damir, two, and Aydin, eight months

5 Sleep solutions
from six months

Ready for sleep training?

Six months marks a major turning point in your baby's first year. It's now that you can seek some real sleep solutions if you want to – if your baby won't settle in the evening or is waking at night – in the form of sleep training.

Most experts believe you should wait until the six month point before embarking on a programme like those outlined below. Waiting until then means you can rest assured your baby is quite ready, because a normal, healthy six-month-old who's begun to take solid food in the day will be physiologically capable of settling herself to sleep at bedtime, and back to sleep in the night, without a feed. And at six months – as long as she's getting loads of love and cuddles from you in the daytime – she should also be emotionally secure enough to cope without you at bedtime and throughout the night, too.

> *Maggie says:* It can still be normal for babies to be waking up before six months, although many are beginning to sleep through the night from about four or five months. I certainly wouldn't try any sort of sleep training before six months.

Habit, not hunger

It's always worth ruling out any medical causes – there's more on these in chapter seven, and you should see your GP if in any doubt – but, in most cases, a baby of six months who's repeatedly unable to settle to sleep alone in the evening, or after waking in the night (or both) will be doing so due to habit. She's probably become used to you providing her with a feed, cuddle, attention of some sort, or whatever other sleep 'cue' or 'association' (see page 71) she needs to get her off, or back, to sleep. You just need to teach her that she doesn't actually need these things . . . and that she can get back to sleep all on her own.

Look at it long-term

While rarely easy – and sometimes very hard indeed – sleep training should be viewed as a challenging but short-term solution to a long-term problem, which, for most people, simply can't go on without their physical or emotional health being compromised. And parents who make a success of sleep training rarely look back: once you're getting a good night's sleep, every night, you begin to understand that the hassle of sleep training was a small and necessary price to pay.

Picking your moment

Be sure before you start that the timing *is* right. Don't be tempted to sleep train if there's some other form of major disruption going on in your baby's life – if you've just gone back to work, for example, or moved house – and always allow enough time after any such event for your little one to become settled again (if you're hoping to get it sorted before a return to work, give yourself at least a month).

In particular, watch for periods of separation anxiety, a very normal developmental phase that can kick in after six months (although it's most common at eight or nine months – making it a good idea to get your sleep problem sussed *before* then if you can). Separation anxiety can strike as your baby's awareness of the world around her develops, causing her to feel genuinely panic-stricken when you leave the room, for fear you will not return. Your best bet if she's affected is to avoid sleep training during this phase (it's always temporary), or to opt for a gentle method like gradual retreat (see below). Don't kick off a sleep-training programme if your little one is suffering physically for any reason either. However, temporary problems such as illness don't mean you should retract on any other good sleep habits you've worked hard to establish, such as a consistent bedtime routine (see page 71), well-spaced night feeds (see page 81) or putting your baby down while she's awake to encourage her to self-settle (see page 76). There's more on the subject in chapter seven.

If your baby has slept in your room for the recommended six months and you're making plans to put her into a room of her own, you might want to make this move first and get her used to a new environment before embarking on sleep training. On the other hand, it can work well to make this move *and* sleep train simultaneously, tackling the two challenges in one go.

Pinpointing the problem

Next, sit down and work out exactly what the problem is. In particular, try to identify any sleep cues or associations that you're providing for your baby. Most experts say it's a good idea to keep a sleep diary for a while before embarking on any kind of training programme. It's a great way to assess the situation in an objective way and, if you've got to a point where you're really fed up about it, it can offer an immediate boost to the spirits because you're already taking the first step in your plan of action.

Aim to keep your diary for one to two weeks so you can build a full picture of what's happening – and try to keep it somewhere accessible, and fill it in when events occur, even at night (it's amazing how quickly you forget exactly what happened, and when, if you're fuzzy with sleep). A clock with bold, illuminated digits is also useful so you know what time it is in the dead of night. You'll find a sleep assessment form online on the Netmums website, which can be downloaded and printed off. But if you want to write your own, include whatever you feel is relevant. You might want to record:

- When your baby wakes in the morning – and whether she seems well rested or not.
- When and for how long she naps during the day.
- When she goes to bed in the evening, and how well she settles.
- What time she falls asleep and what, if any, sleep cues she needed to get there.
- When she wakes in the night; how long she is awake for; and how she gets back to sleep.
- Brief thoughts on your own responses and actions.

Once you know exactly what your little one's undesirable sleep habits are, you can think about how to change them. Some experts suggest you set yourself goals and put these down on paper, too, and, if there's more than one problem to tackle, to confront them one by one. So, perhaps your first priority will be getting a calm, regular bedtime in place; maybe your main aim, initially, is to drop one or more night feeds (see below), or to ditch a sleep association that's proving a nuisance, such as a dummy (see page 12). Or maybe you're simply hoping for that elusive uninterrupted night's sleep!

Ditching night-time feeding

At six months your baby may still be feeding one or more times during the night, which means your first challenge will be removing her dependence on this nocturnal snacking. You can safely cut out night feeds from six months – assuming you've made a start on weaning and she's still getting four to five milk feeds in the day, including one shortly before bedtime – because, at this age, your baby has no physical need for them. If she's still demanding them, it's almost certainly habit rather than hunger: she's convinced herself she needs a feed to fall asleep and hence demands one whenever she wakes up to get off again.

You can either choose to go 'cold turkey' and cut out night feeds at once, in conjunction with a sleep-training method, or you can take a more gradual approach, cutting them out one by one, either by increasing the spaces between feeds over a number of days and weeks. (Turn back to page 81 to read more about spacing night feeds.)

Once you've cracked the milk habit, you may find you've also cracked the waking problem – or you may find your baby's still waking in the hope of some alternative comfort, in which case, you'll need to opt for one of the training methods outlined below.

The all-important bedtime routine – *again*!

There's no point in trying any sort of sleep training if you don't have a consistent, well-established bedtime routine in place – it's absolutely key, as any expert will tell you (turn back to page 71 for more on bedtime routines). Apart from providing a reliable pattern and a series of healthy sleep cues for your baby, a good bedtime routine makes sleep training easier because, if you know you've given your baby a lingering, loving end to the day and put her into her cot feeling secure and settled, you won't have to feel bad about being tough later on.

Equally, your baby's daytime schedule counts. She'll probably have settled into a system of fairly regular naps now, typically twice a day, and it's important that she continues to get these in order to make up the full quota of rest she needs (it's variable, but the average six-month-old requires somewhere between 12 and 15 hours' sleep per 24 hours). Nap-time will also prevent her being overtired at night, which can make her stressed and irritable and, ironically, less likely to drop off with ease at bedtime. (If you're having trouble getting your baby to nap enough, turn back to page 91 for some tips.) Although, generally speaking, it's not a good idea to wake your baby when she's sleeping, it's advisable to wake her if she's napping later than 4pm so that she's just the right level of sleepy come bedtime. When you're sleep training, it's important your baby is tired enough to drop off when you put her in her cot – if she's not, try making bedtime a little later and, once you've achieved your goals, you can bring it back to an earlier time gradually, changing it by five minutes at a time, every other day.

Weighing up your options

Read up on the various different strategies before making a decision with your partner. Which one you try is down to you, and will depend on what you and your baby can cope with – although, how desperate and exhausted you are may also influence your choice. As a rule, controlled crying requires nerves of steel and a will of iron, but tends to get you results fast. More 'gentle' methods like gradual retreat, the kissing game, and pick up/put down are less heart-rending, but are likely to take much longer to work.

It's a good idea to chat with your health visitor, too, or a sympathetic GP, and let them know what you're planning. Getting the nod from a relevant professional will help you to feel certain you're doing the right thing.

Don't go it alone

If you're planning to undertake sleep training, make sure you talk it through first with your partner. Parents need to agree 100 per cent that it's the right thing to do and the right method's been chosen, because when the going gets tough in the middle of the night, you *both* need to be determined to see it through.

Discuss beforehand how your 'team' will work. For instance, will you do one night on and one night off; take either the evening, or the night shift; or work on a rota system of hourly slots? Perhaps the stronger of you will volunteer to do the 'tough' bit, while the other provides refreshments and moral support (and, in the dead of night, has permission to put their head under the pillow).

Of course, dads don't get off the hook because they have to go to work the next day, or they can't face the crying. In fact, many couples find that Dad is the best person to do the difficult bit, because mums – especially if they're the one around most during the day – tend to have more invested emotionally, and babies will often exploit that. (And dads are definitely the best people to take over if you're trying to cut down on, or cut out, night-time breastfeeds: bursting boobs and a baby who can smell your milk will only make trying to be firm even tougher.)

For lone parents, sleep training can be particularly hard work. If you don't have a partner around, you may have to think carefully about which method you can best cope with. Or you may want to rope in a good friend or close relative to help you out, perhaps in the evening slot, or even overnight if you can persuade them to stay. Include them in your plans, and make sure you are both reading from exactly the same song sheet.

Louise says: It's a good idea to have a sleep-training buddy – a friend who's been through it, a sympathetic health visitor, or perhaps another Netmum who you can call or message in the morning for support, especially if the night before was lousy and you made little or no progress. When I was sleep training my daughter I'd got nowhere after a week, but each morning I'd call my friend, who's also a health visitor, and she urged me to keep going. One week later, we cracked it!

Maggie says: Support is crucial when you are doing sleep training. If you're on your own or have an unsupportive partner, keep a list of people you can call on for back up when the going gets really tough. In the day, accept help from friends or family so you can have a short break to recharge your batteries and get some much needed rest.

Get your head in the game

Once you've decided which method you want to go for, really resolve to go for it. It's important to be positive in your approach – at the start and throughout, too. In the midst of a sleep-training programme, you may find yourself crying harder than your baby, or feeling angry and resentful about how it's dominating your life. But even the youngest of babies can read her mum's emotions and be influenced by them. So you need to keep your feelings well hidden.

However, don't forget to be realistic, too. Sleep training *can* work quickly and easily, but it can also be a long haul, requiring massive determination. You may also have to accept that a particular method isn't working for you and find you need to change tack, beginning all over again from square one.

The good news is, though, that if you do it right, whichever method you go for should get you a result. (Although it's very likely to get worse before it gets better, so be prepared for that, too.)

Louise says: Don't try to sleep train unless you're in a good place. If you're on edge, or rowing a lot with your partner, or you've got a work deadline to meet, it's not going to be a good time. You need to focus your emotional reserves on it – if they're tied up elsewhere, forget it. And be realistic. Don't assume you're going to do it overnight, or that it will be easy. It might be horrendous and it will certainly be hard work, quite possibly for several weeks or more. Equally, it's important to be optimistic, and to stay positive. If the going gets tough, tell yourself it will all be worthwhile to have a baby who sleeps all night.

Choosing to go with the flow

Of course, sleep training is by no means compulsory. Perhaps you're happy to carry on feeding your baby at night, enjoy co-sleeping and going to bed at the same time, or don't mind how long it takes to cuddle or rock her back to sleep whenever she demands. Maybe you'd rather wait until she's a bit older, or maybe you're happy to carry on as you are until the day she makes her own changes. If everyone's getting sufficient sleep, your baby's appetite in the daytime isn't being compromised by night feeding, and your other relationships are not being affected for the worse, then carry on as you are.

If you do choose this route, though, bear in mind that sleep training – while quite possible with older babies and children – tends to get trickier the longer you leave it. And leaving it indefinitely means you could be looking at this lifestyle for a long time to come. True, she'll sleep through without you or move into her own bed at some point in the future but it could be a long way off – possibly years. You'll also need to give some thought to what happens when subsequent babies arrive.

Louise says: For many parents, sleep training is not even a consideration. They're happy to be called upon for their child's every need, in fact they enjoy it and can survive on frequently broken sleep. However, it may well be that these parents are less stressed and perhaps work fewer hours, hence there's less pressure to get a full night's sleep. These babes will, in time, achieve uninterrupted sleep by themselves. I say, each to their own.

Maggie says: Sleep training is a very emotive subject and everyone has their own views on it. I recommend that parents follow their own instincts and do what they feel comfortable with. If the night waking is not causing either parent a problem, then don't worry about it. Ignore other people's well-meant advice. If you decide on a sleep-training programme, choose one you all feel happy about. Take time out to nurture yourself, though, if you are having broken nights and enlist as much help and support as you can from friends and family.

Controlled crying

You may hear this strategy called Ferberizing, after one of its foremost advocates, the US paediatrician Dr Richard Ferber. Dr Ferber himself prefers to call it 'progressive waiting'. It's also known as 'crying it out' (CIO), 'the checking method' and 'graduated extinction'.

Controlled crying is very effective if done correctly and usually works fast – within a week, normally, although you should be prepared to keep at it for a fortnight if necessary. And it comes recommended by many experts, as well as countless parents who've used it and got results. However, it has its critics and it's definitely not for the fainthearted – some people just find it too hard leaving their baby to cry. If you do try it, get ready for a potentially tough time and prepare to be super-committed to see it through.

You should use exactly the same procedure to get your baby settled at bedtime and settled after she subsequently wakes up.

Before you start . . .

- If you haven't already, ensure you've got a very well-established, consistent bedtime in place.
- Get the timing right. Make sure you have at least a week ahead of you, at home, with nothing else on. Don't attempt it if your baby's poorly, teething, has just been immunised, is still genuinely hungry at night, or is going through any sort of emotional instability.
- Do your research so you know exactly what you're doing. Controlled crying won't harm your baby if you do it right, but it might if you don't.
- Get your other half on board. Controlled crying is particularly tough if you're doing it singlehanded, so get help if you're a lone parent. Consistency is key, so make

sure anyone else who's going to be involved knows exactly how the strategy will work.

- Let your neighbours know what you're planning, if they're likely to be disturbed.
- Move older siblings to a room where they won't be woken or, better still, arrange for them to stay with a good friend or relative for the period. (There are more solutions for siblings on page 151.)
- Be strong and optimistic. You're unlikely to make it work for you if you're depressed or anxious.

How it's done

- Make sure your baby has her usual evening feed and bedtime. Be sure to give her lots of cuddles and talk quietly and soothingly to her. Put her in her cot while she's drowsy, but still awake. Quietly say 'goodnight' and leave the room.
- Ignore any grizzling or whining. Once she starts crying in earnest, leave her for three to five minutes at first (depending on how long you can cope) before going back to check on her. Don't turn on the lights, touch her, or make eye contact. Say something calm and reassuring to her, like, 'Time to go to sleep now. Shh.' (And use that same phrase subsequently.) Stick around for no longer than a minute or two, regardless of whether your baby stops crying or not. Tempting as it is to hang around outside the door, it's better to get on with the ironing or watch television.
- As she continues to cry, you can lengthen the amount of time in between checks by three to five minutes. Eventually you can leave her for up to 15 or 20 minutes (if you can't

handle that – and it can seem like a lifetime in the middle of the night – try sticking with ten). Have a watch or clock nearby so you can be sure you've got the timings right.

- Each time you go in to check, repeat your reassuring phrase but remember it is better not to touch her or make eye contact. Do your utmost to remain calm and unemotional yourself.

- Don't go out of earshot while your baby is crying, but do try to find something to do in order to busy yourself and to take your mind off what's happening.

- If you're lucky, you won't have to go through this process for much more than an hour or two before your baby drops off. However, don't be surprised if she keeps up with the crying for longer still.

- Remember that – if you want it to work – you simply mustn't give in. A few babies become so distressed during controlled crying that they end up vomiting. If you can handle it, calmly clear up and continue.

- Wait for a good half an hour after all goes quiet before going in to check one last time, to make sure she's definitely asleep. You don't want to rouse her after all that hard work.

- There may be a 'test time' on the third or fourth night as your baby makes a final attempt to foil you in your efforts. Stick with it.

Maggie says: If you can't bear to hear the crying and it's getting to you, give yourself a break for five minutes and get out of earshot, perhaps listen to some loud music. A baby's cry is designed to upset you and not be ignored, which is why so many parents find this approach tough. When you go in to check, you need to be like a robot. Don't make eye contact, don't kiss or cuddle, have a blank face. It's counter-effective to pat or stroke. However, if they're sobbing their heart out and you really need to calm them, I would suggest briefly picking them up with their face over your shoulder, holding them quietly until their breathing returns to normal, and then putting them down again. You could also put a hand on their back, or just hover your hand over their body so you're not touching, but they know you are there. It requires incredible determination. You have to keep going, even if it means you're up all night, otherwise you'll reinforce the message that if they shout for long enough they'll eventually get what they want. Once they realise you mean business and you're going to follow through, they will learn that it simply isn't worth the effort. If one night you just can't face it, then give in straight away and start afresh the next night.

Louise says: You have to try not to let your own frustration and upset show because, if your baby picks up on those emotions, she's likely to follow suit. You need to avoid crying, even though that's exactly what you feel like doing. It's certainly true that consistency is key. But don't beat yourself up on the first night if you don't manage it. If you do have to stop, pledge to start over again the following night. And if you really can't cope, think about another method. It's horses for courses – you should do whatever works for you.

Is it cruel to leave my baby crying?

Some people do question the wisdom of controlled crying techniques and it has its critics among experts, such as child psychotherapist Dr

Margot Sunderland, author of *What Every Parent Needs to Know: The remarkable effects of love, nurture and play on your child's development*. She believes that leaving a baby to cry for prolonged periods releases high levels of stress chemicals, potentially causing long-term emotional or psychological damage. And, of course, some parents just don't feel able to see through a programme of controlled crying, which is understandable – after all, it goes against your instincts as loving parents to ignore your baby determinedly when she's distressed.

However, the view of most experts in child health, development and psychology, is that leaving your baby to cry for short periods will not be harmful, as long as you never leave her crying for more than 20 minutes without checking. No one these days recommends a 'cold turkey' or 'total extinction' approach – in other words, simply leaving your baby alone until she cries herself to sleep.

If you find it impossibly hard not to touch your baby when she's upset, you may want to try a variation of controlled crying which uses 'repetitive reassurance' – touching, patting, or stroking her briefly to comfort her when you go in to check. Most experts say it's not ideal, as it gives a mixed message – that your baby *will* get some kind of reward if she cries for long enough. Others say it can still work, but is likely to prolong the process.

> **Maggie says:** If a child is very distressed and upset they secrete high levels of the stress hormone cortisol, which research suggests is not good for their brain development. However, many sleep experts and psychologists believe that controlled crying, if done correctly, will not cause irreparable harm to any child who is loved and cherished, and has all their needs met, by their parents throughout the rest of the day. It's certainly a very effective method of sleep training but it can be incredibly hard to do.

Dr David says: There's no published evidence that controlled crying causes long-term harm to children or that it leads to a change in infant-parent attachment relationships. However, it's not for everyone and some families might prefer the more gradual techniques, though they tend to take longer. A lot of parents are worried their child might be crying due to something else. It is unlikely to be something else, though, if your child otherwise appears healthy, is not having any problems during the day, and the crying quickly settles on handling. But, if you're worried, then of course you should seek medical advice.

Gradual withdrawal

You might hear this method referred to as 'gradual retreat', 'gradual distancing', 'the disappearing chair method', 'fading' or 'camping out'. It involves little or no crying, so you don't have to go through the torment of listening to your baby screaming, and it won't disturb older siblings or the neighbours. It's likely to take much longer than controlled crying, though, and is still potentially very hard work!

Gradual withdrawal is a good method to use if your baby needs physical contact from you in order to go to sleep, or if you're trying to move her out of your bed and into a cot of her own. It's also a good bet for older babies and toddlers, although you may have to try a different variation if you're using it for a child who's in a bed and able to get out at will (see page 148). As with controlled crying, use these techniques to get your baby settled at bedtime, as well as when she wakes in the night.

Before you start . . .

- Make sure you've got an established, consistent bedtime in place. It's just as important with this sort of method.

- Get the timing right. Choose a period where there'll be no upheaval or nights away – and bear in mind it may take closer to a month for this to succeed. Don't *start* this method if your little one is suffering physically or emotionally for some reason – however, unlike controlled crying, you have scope to carry on with it if a problem such as minor illness, teething, or separation anxiety crops up halfway through.

- Do your research so you know exactly what you're doing. This still goes without saying!

- Make sure your other half's on board. While perhaps less emotionally draining than controlled crying, gradual withdrawal is still physically exhausting, time-sapping and very, very tedious. So you're just as likely to need support with it.

- Be strong and optimistic. Don't underestimate the willpower you need to undertake this method, just because it's gentler. And it's going to take longer, so you'll need to be determined for longer.

How it's done

- Carry out your baby's bedtime as normal, with all the usual calming conditions, and put your baby into her cot when she's drowsy but still awake.

- Tuck her in, say a brief goodnight, and take a seat by her side, making physical contact by holding her hand or stroking her. (If your little one is used to you lying down next to her, you can start off doing this – some parents set up a camp bed or mattress for the purpose. You can move on to a sitting position in the next stage.)

- Don't make eye contact, talk or sing to your baby, or engage with her other than to hold her hand or stroke her. Use a boring, repetitive phrase, like, 'It's bedtime now, goodnight.' (You can help remain 'unavailable' to her – and relieve boredom at the same time – by reading a book. Try to keep page-rustling to a minimum, though.)
- After two to three nights in one position, change it slightly – if you're sitting on a chair, move it back a short distance. Two to three nights later, you can move the chair back another foot or so.
- Eventually, you can put the chair in the doorway and a few nights later, you can move it outside. You can keep reappearing in the doorway every few minutes, and gradually increase the length of time before you appear, perhaps pottering around upstairs doing jobs while they drop off. Your baby should then become confident enough to cope when you finally disappear from her sight.
- Continue ignoring your baby, other than to repeat quietly your 'boring' phrase, even if she tries to engage with you.

Two more 'gentle' methods

The kissing game

Also known as 'kiss and retreat', or 'the elastic band method', this is similar to gradual withdrawal, in that you never go far from your baby's side while she's awake. It's good for babies who need you around in order to drop off, and should be preceded by a well-established and relaxed bedtime routine, with your baby put into her cot while sleepy, but awake.

- Kiss your baby goodnight and back off, but don't leave the room.
- Keep returning to your baby every few minutes to give her a kiss. Move around the room a little in between, perhaps tidying up.
- If she cries, go back to kiss her briefly and at regular intervals until she's asleep.
- A pat or stroke can be substituted for the kiss (especially if all that bending down is making your back hurt).
- In theory, each night it will take less time and fewer kisses for your baby to drop off until, eventually, they don't need you in the room at all in order to do so.

Pick up/put down

This method comes from Tracy Hogg, otherwise known as the 'Baby Whisperer', and involves repeated picking up and putting down of your baby – so it's not going to be much cop for anyone with a bad back. It could be for you if you really can't bear to ignore your baby at all. Bear in mind this is a brief summary, and there are variations according to age, so if you want to try it at home, you'll need the book (see the further reading section on page 181 for details).

- Go to your baby once she starts crying. At first, use comforting words and a hand on her back to reassure her.
- If that doesn't stop her crying, pick her up. Keep a hand on her back and repeat a phrase like, 'It's sleep time, darling.'
- Put her back down in the cot the second she stops crying (don't wait for her to drop off). If she starts crying before you've had a chance to lie her down, lie her down anyway before picking her up again.
- Repeat the process until your baby is asleep. As the nights go on, in theory, you will have to pick up and put down fewer times until, eventually, she will settle without you.

Starting all over again

Generally, once you've cracked sleep training, you've cracked it. But sometimes, something will happen to overturn any positive sleep habits your baby has adopted – you returning to work, moving house, a holiday, illness, separation anxiety, or teething, for example.

At times like these, you may find you have to go through your chosen sleep-training method again. The good news is that if it worked once before, chances are it will work much quicker a second time.

What the netmums say

Sleep training

When he was around seven months he was trying to fight bedtime and naps, so I used the pick up/put down method – you pick them up if they are crying and as soon as they stop, they go back down. You can end up doing this around twenty times or more, depending on how strong-willed your little one is, but I found I only had to do it a couple of times before his resolve broke!
Deborah from Bexley, mum to Thomas, one

I used the controlled crying method for all three of my sons. I let them sleep in my bed with me until they no longer needed feeding in the night, up until that point they were all rocked to sleep, too. But once I moved them into their own room in their own cribs, I would give them their feed, have a cuddle and sing a lullaby, and then put them down while they were still awake. All three screamed terribly the first night, but all three slept through for 11 hours after a week. It's the best thing I ever did as a parent. For me it meant a proper night's

sleep and it taught the kids how to settle themselves without me. It might not be for everyone, but it was a Godsend for us.
Jade from St Ives, mum to Daniel, four, Antonio, three, and Rafael, nine months

I've never been able to leave my daughter to cry. It's just something I've never found easy, even though I know some friends of mine who do and, to be honest, most of the time it seems to work. But rightly or wrongly, I couldn't do it. I think it's all down to personalities – yours and your baby's!
Nova from Manchester, mum to Poppy, three

By the time my daughter was 11 months I was at my wits' end. She would not go to sleep unless I stayed with her and some nights it would take two hours to get her to sleep. I was suffering from depression, and it was putting a real strain on the relationships between my daughter, me and my partner. A friend told me about the controlled crying technique. It sounded so easy and a miracle answer. So I spent a week looking on the internet at different techniques and chose the one on Jo Frost's website. I prepared myself and my partner for a tough first night. Night one was horrendous: it took ages before she dropped off. Both my partner and I were mentally exhausted. Night two was pretty bad as well. Night three was better. Night four? Well, a miracle! She was asleep in two minutes. It was the best (and hardest) thing we've ever done as parents.
Susan from Salisbury, mum to Darcey, one

My son is still waking in the night for a breastfeed at seven months and I'm currently trying the kiss and retreat method. Although it was hard last night (the first night without a night feed) we did it and he (eventually) got off to sleep after five

to six disturbances. The idea is that you are reinforcing to your child that you will *always* come back when you leave! We're still a long way off, but I hope this is the answer.
Katie from Sunderland, mum to Morgan, ten months

We don't believe in controlled crying and, if that's the case, I don't think there's much you can do to make your child sleep through. Samantha started sleeping through the night quite often at 11 months, which was when everything got a lot easier – up until then she woke us two or three times a night. I'm still breastfeeding her and sometimes she drops off in my arms if she's very tired, but is also happy to fall asleep by herself, holding her 'blankie' and sucking her thumb. We do think a bedtime routine is important. She always has a bath about 6pm and is usually asleep before 7pm.
Dinah from Harrow, mum to Samantha, one

We decided to let our son Joshy decide when he was ready to sleep through, as we did with our older son who, by five months, was sleeping soundly for a full 12 hours. However, this just didn't happen with Joshy, who kept waking every night at least once, sometimes up to four or five times. We spoke to the health visitor who explained all the techniques and advised us to pick one that we felt most comfortable with. So we tried controlled crying and, after just three nights, we noticed the difference – he was going through every night until 6.15am. My husband and I felt like brand new people. Now he'll sleep through at least 11 hours a night and he is so much happier in the daytime, too. We are all so much happier, in fact. I only wish I had done something sooner.
Jo from Barry, mum to Hayden, five, and Joshy, two

6 Sleep solutions for older babies and toddlers

Still waking . . . or waking again?

Plenty of parents are still in need of sleep solutions once their baby is past their first birthday. It may be you've *always* had a problem with settling and/or night wakings, but it's only now that you have got round to doing anything about it. Or perhaps you cracked sleep problems earlier – or were even lucky enough not to have had any – but something has happened to change that situation.

The sleep solutions available to you may be a little different with an older baby. For one thing, developmental progress – while a joy to behold during the day – can cause a few problems at night. If your baby is standing or walking, he may feel very proud of himself and be keen to try these skills out at bedtime, too, or be eager to exploit them when he wakes at night. And he's becoming increasingly sociable and communicative, which might make him less inclined to settle down when you need him to. Emotional issues such as separation anxiety [see page 105] can also kick in, commonly from around eight months, and physical matters like teething or illness can also prompt setbacks.

In any case, you don't have to worry about it being 'too late' to fix a sleeping problem. It's still perfectly do-able even after your baby's reached his first birthday.

Louise says: It doesn't matter how good your routine is, or how effective your sleep training proved to be, chances are you'll need to revisit old ground at some point, for reasons beyond your control – illness, teething, noisy visitors, going on holiday. As long as you revert to a normal routine once the disruption is over, you should be fine, and even if not, you can usually rely on a much shorter 'refresher period' of sleep training to get you back on track.

What the netmums say

Still waking . . . or waking again?

We had a silly problem that had a big impact when my son was around ten months – he learned to stand up but couldn't get himself back down. So he'd get up in the night and need someone to go in and lay him down, then he would go straight back to sleep. We had found he slept better in a sleeping bag for the warmth but, amazingly, this solved the standing problem, too; we just fastened the end of the bag so there was no wriggle room and when he could no longer get up so easily, he just gave up and went back to sleep. We were all happier.

Ruth from Leatherhead, mum to Ethan, five

I was in desperation as, at nearly two, my daughter had only slept through a couple of times in her life. At one point I was getting up to give her a bottle up to eight times a night – ridiculous, I know! I was beginning to resent her for what felt like a miserable existence. My health visitor arranged for me to go to daily play classes to try and wear her out a bit more, which definitely helped (and also made me feel better about my daughter). I also tried putting a stairgate across her bedroom door, to stop her leaving her bedroom at night to come looking for me. And I now put a small bottle of milk by her bed so when she wakes, she gets up, has a drink and goes back to sleep. It's worked so far.

Marni from Northampton, mum to Hannah, four, and Tabitha, two

We travelled abroad when Callum was nine months and, on our return, because of the time difference, he woke the first night at 5am, wanting milk, which I gave him. But he began waking at this time every night after that. I thought he was probably doing it out of habit, so the next night, when he woke at 5am, I just gave him water. This seemed to cure it and he went back to sleeping straight through the night again. So I think if an older baby is waking at night, it's probably not genuine hunger. My advice would be to try giving water, to break the habit. Most babies would think it's not worth waking up for that.

Eleanor from Inverness, mum to Callum, one

Our eldest son started waking at around ten months old, having slept through most nights from six weeks. Initially we'd go to his room, comfort him, not pick him up, not make eye contact, etc. But my heart bled every time I left him. I'm a bit of a softy and used to spend hours sitting next to his cot waiting for him to fall asleep. I was working part-time and felt like a zombie. Eventually, my husband and I decided to take him into bed with us whenever he woke at night, and he'd sleep like a dream! We got a bit firmer with him when our second son arrived, letting him cry for a while and then comforting him. After a while he slept for much longer stretches in his own cot. He's in a big boy's bed now, although he still joins us at around 6.30am and sleeps for another half an hour.

Irma from Oldham, mum to Damir, two, and Aydin, eight months

I'm currently breastfeeding my youngest child. She's almost nine months and still waking several times for feeds during the night. I'd love to get her to sleep through but I know this is a short-term thing and I'm sure she'll sleep through soon. It's a bit of a shock to the system because my other three slept through from about eight weeks.

Sharon from Sherburn in Elmet, mum to Kevin, 22, Sarah, 19, Isabel, four, and Charlotte, nine months

My daughter had been a fantastic sleeper from ten weeks. She'd go down at 7pm and not stir until 7 or 8am. Suddenly, at 11 months, she started waking several times during the night, crying. It was our initial assumption that she was hungry and so we'd give her a bottle, and bulk up her meals during the day to ensure that hunger wasn't the problem. It continued for several months and we were getting to the end of our tether, trying to work out what the problem was. To this day, we still don't know. However, after approximately one week of ditching the night-time bottle and using a controlled crying technique, she's back to her old self, sleeping for 12 hours. It was hard listening to her cry during that week, but not nearly as hard as it was being up most of the night for several months and spending the days feeling snappy and irritable.

Melissa from Lancaster, mum to Annabelle, one

My eldest suffered terribly from night terrors as a younger baby and would wake up ten times a night screaming. It would take me hours to settle him back to sleep and, eventually, I had to put a bed in his room and stay with him. This carried on for around eight months or so. We moved house when he was 15 months old and, since I was also seven months pregnant, we decorated a bedroom for him and took him shopping for a 'big boy's bed'. Then we set up a new bedtime routine. It took a few nights of him getting out of bed crying to come back downstairs, but he soon realised that bedtime was final and, from then on, he started sleeping much better. My younger son has only slept through the night twice. He still wakes in the night for a drink of milk. I've come to the exhausting conclusion that my boys are just not great sleepers.

Chantelle from Bushey, mum to Kai, two, and Ollie, 11 months

Good sleep habits for older babies

There are lots of helpful things you can do generally to help your older baby sleep better (many of which you may already be doing: in which case, keep up the good work).

- Get some fresh air every day and encourage lots of active play, which will help to tire him out.
- Make sure your baby still gets the daytime naps he needs

– but not *more* than he needs. For more on naps and the older baby, see below.

- Stick to a regular bedtime routine as far as possible, even if upheaval of some sort makes things tricky. If you've never had a bedtime routine in place, why not start one now? And if you had one before, but have gone off track for some reason, aim to reinstate it. For more on bedtime routines and the older baby, see below.

- Make the hour or so before bedtime a calm time, by sticking to quiet activities like drawing and reading, and avoiding rough-and-tumble games, or noisy TV and DVDs (with the exception of favourite programmes designed with bedtime in mind).

- Once your baby's fully weaned and eating a fairly normal diet, be careful what you give him to eat and drink in the hours leading up to bedtime. Foods to avoid include caffeine, sugar and certain additives. Good pre-bedtime foods include carbohydrates and anything containing tryptophan, an amino acid with naturally occurring sedative properties. There's a bit more about it in the following chapter.

Bedtimes for older babies

A consistent bedtime routine remains a key healthy sleep habit for your baby (and for you, too, if peaceful, child-free evenings are important to you). Do stick with it if you've successfully managed one so far and remember, all the same rules still apply: make it happy; don't allow it to become a drawn-out affair; stick to your rituals; keep your 'goodnights' firm and brief; and always leave your baby to settle on his own.

Try your utmost to keep bedtime schedules on the go even if some sort of upheaval threatens to upend it — illness; separation anxiety; a house move; you returning to work; the introduction of a new caregiver, for example. A child of one or two shouldn't need a revised bedtime, as his reduced sleep needs should be reflected in the dropping of daytime naps (see page 138) but if your older baby seems less tired or less inclined to settle in the evening, try indulging in a later bedtime for a while, settling him with the usual routine when he seems ready. If you want, you can then return it to an earlier time by moving it back, in small increments of ten to 15 minutes, every few days. Reluctance to settle at bedtime could also be a sign that he's getting more daytime sleep than he needs – perhaps he's ready to drop a nap (see below), in which case, you can help him adjust by altering his usual daytime schedule.

If you've never had a bedtime routine (see page 71), it's by no means too late to start one – although you may need a little extra commitment and patience in doing so. There's probably no point in trying to start a routine early in the evening if your baby doesn't normally settle until fairly late: he's unlikely to go down without a struggle if he's not ready. So start it late if need be, then work on bringing it back to an earlier time in small steps.

Sleep training an older baby

If you're having problems settling your older baby in the evening and/or he's still waking once or more in the night, you don't have to settle for this if you don't want to. Just because you missed the earlier window doesn't mean you can't sleep train now: read on to find out how. Sleep training an older baby may be a slightly longer process, as there are added challenges. Mobility is the main problem. Once they've started crawling, standing, cruising or walking, babies can (and often will) get up and move about once you've put them down, adding a whole new dimension to the business of settling them and keeping them settled. They may even start to climb out of the cot or, if you've got to the point where you've transferred them to a bed, actually to get up and come downstairs to find you. Not only that, but older babies have minds of their own and are often keen to show it! It's all part and parcel of a healthy development process ... not that that's much consolation when you're tired and they're playing up.

To bed to sleep?

Some sleep-training techniques for toddlers assume you're not necessarily looking to get them to sleep, but simply into bed (and staying there). As time goes on and life becomes more interesting, some older babies do take longer to drop off after bedtime but, as long as your little one spends the time chattering to himself, singing, quietly playing or looking at a book, rather than getting up, coming downstairs or making a very disruptive protest, that's an acceptable compromise. As long as he's in bed, he'll be relaxed and resting – and you'll be enjoying a peaceful evening.

Maggie says: With any sleep-training programme, at any age, it's really important to meet all your child's needs for attention during the day. If you have a busy life and other children, your little one may feel he's missing out on your attention in the day. Children will go to any lengths to get attention – even negative attention is better than being ignored, and sometimes this is the underlying cause of a sleep problem. So try to spend some one-to-one time every day with your child, and let them know how special they are. Pay positive attention when they do what you want and ignore minor misbehaviour. Bear in mind the old adage: 'What we pay attention to is what we get more of.'

Gradual retreat or the kissing game

What is it?

The advantages of these two methods over controlled crying techniques are that they are less upsetting and there is less noise involved. So they're good to use for an older baby suffering from separation anxiety, for example, or who is generally anxious, or perhaps if you're trying to keep the noise down because there's either a young baby or an older sibling in the house who you don't want to disturb. Expect these methods to take a while – up to a month or longer is not unusual.

How does it work?

For older babies and toddlers, you can use exactly the same techniques as outlined on pages 118 and 120. If your little one is mobile and getting out of bed, you may have to employ a rapid return strategy at the same time! (See below.)

Choice and consequence

What is it?

This is a useful tactic for a toddler who won't stay in his bed. And although it works best for older children who are mature enough to grasp the concept, it can work well with babies as young as 18 months, who'll very soon get the picture.

How does it work?

You say to your child that if he lies quietly you will stay in the room with him, but if he doesn't get into bed and go to sleep, you will leave. You must then follow through on this promise, leaving the room if he gets out of bed or refuses to settle. In theory, if you're consistent, you will break the habit and, in time, be able to leave the room before he's dropped off. If not, you may need to move on to a gradual withdrawal approach in order to teach him to settle without you there.

Maggie says: With choice and consequence, you have a dialogue along the following lines with your child: 'You can either choose to stay in the bed quietly [a positive behaviour choice] or you can choose to get out of bed [a negative choice]. If you choose to stay in bed quietly [positive behaviour], I will sit with you [positive consequence]. If you choose not to stay in bed [negative behaviour], I will leave the room and the stairgate will be put across the door [negative consequence]. It's up to you – it's your choice.' By offering limited choices and consequences you are rewarding the positive behaviour you want and giving some control to the child who can choose wisely or not. It can be surprisingly effective!

Rapid return

What is it?

This is a good tactic to employ with a toddler who's leaving his bed or room after being settled, or during the night.

How does it work?

It involves staying calm and taking him gently but firmly by the hand, and leading him back to bed. The aim is to remain silent and unresponsive while tucking him in, say goodnight, and then leave the room without being drawn by any pleas for more attention. Of course, there's nothing stopping him from getting out of bed again – and he probably will. This is where you have to repeat the process – and be prepared to do so many times. If you're committed and you keep doing this as often and for as long as needed, eventually he'll realise there's no point in continuing and give up.

Door shutting

What is it?

This is an extension of controlled crying or checking-based tactics, and it allows for the added challenge of a mobile toddler who is getting out of bed. As with controlled crying, it can result in a lot of tears and it's not for the faint-hearted – or a good idea if your child has an anxious nature, is poorly, or having to deal with any other upheaval at the time.

How does it work?

When your baby gets out of bed, you respond by telling him you will hold the door shut if he does not go back. You follow through your threat if he gets out of bed again, shutting the door (and holding it shut if he tries to open it) for a minute. If he still hasn't returned to bed after this time, hold the door shut for another two minutes, then for three, then for four, and for up to five minutes. Don't engage in a conversation, other than to repeat calmly that you will keep shutting the door unless he returns to bed. Keep repeating this process as often as necessary, until your little one understands he's getting nowhere, gives up and goes to sleep.

The drawback of door shutting is that it can become a battle of wills, and a physical one at that, if your little one decides to make a determined effort to yank the door open from inside his room. An alternative, which gets round this problem, is to fix a stairgate across the doorframe – that way he can at least see out and you can reassure him during checks face-to-face (for safety reasons, you need to be very certain it's fixed securely, as well as being alert to the possibility that your child will try to climb over it. You also need to make sure the room is clear of any obvious hazards should he fling himself around in tantrum mode). Or you could take a tip from Dr Christopher Green, author of *Toddler Taming*: loop a rope around your child's inner door handle, fixing the end to another door handle (or some other firm point) nearby, leaving enough slack that the child can open the door just wide enough to see out.

Some parents fix a lock to their child's door for the same effect but it's probably not a great idea: apart from being a potentially frightening experience for them, it could be risky in the event of a fire.

> ***Louise says:*** Door shutting can be tricky. It can often cause meltdown and it's important to ensure that the bedroom is a safe place so a tantrumming toddler can't injure himself. It doesn't always work, and may in fact make things worse if your little one ends up so distraught from being shut in that he needs comfort.

Reward systems

What is it?

Setting up some kind of simple 'incentive scheme' for positive achievements, like staying in bed when you ask them to or getting through the night without waking you, can be effective for toddlers of just under two or more (more complex reward schemes such as those involving sticker charts only start to be workable from the age of three), as well as providing a gentle, positive reinforcement for when methods such as gradual withdrawal or door shutting are proving successful.

How does it work?

One lovely and well-tested idea is the use of 'magic fairy dust' – if your child has behaved the way you hoped for, you sprinkle a little glitter over their pillow and perhaps on the window sill, then tell them the magic sleep fairy (or elf, or whatever!) has paid a visit and is so pleased she's left some magic dust for them.

What the netmums say

Sleep training for older babies

Jude was 15 months old and still being rocked off to sleep by the time we came to sleep train him, using gradual withdrawal. We'd tried controlled crying before but it made him anxious, so we waited a while before looking for a different method. I started by explaining I was going to sit on the chair until he fell asleep, but that I wasn't going to talk to him because it was night-time and he needed to go to sleep in peace and quiet. After the bedtime routine I sat in a chair right by the bed, with my book to keep me occupied, not interacting with him, and stayed that way until he fell asleep (which took longer than an hour as he kept trying to talk to me and get my attention). Then I quietly left the room. When he woke in the night I went back and sat in the chair and said, 'It's night-time, goodnight,' and nothing else until he fell back asleep. Each night he'd go to sleep quicker and after a few days I moved the chair a bit further away from the bed, until eventually it was out of the room. Sometimes he started to get panicky when I moved the chair, so I'd move it back to the previous spot for a while. It took three months in all! It was a long haul, but I didn't mind – after a year of sleepless nights it was worth the effort. And since then, he's

gone off to sleep by himself with no problems and when he wakes at night he settles himself off without needing me.
Jenna from Wolverhampton, mum to Jude, two, and Arabella, eight months

From birth Lucy was hard to settle and I would always breastfeed her to sleep. In the night I was quick to pick her up when she cried, for fear of her waking our older daughter. She had to hold hands with me through the cot to fall asleep, and most nights she would end up in our bed. Then when she went in her own room, one of us always ended up sleeping in with her – if we tried to leave her to sleep alone she would wake every few hours and it was exhausting. We tried gradual retreat several times, and controlled crying once, which was really not for us. Eventually we just accepted she needed us next to her to sleep. (My eldest slept through every night after six months, so I know it's just down to the different personalities.) Then one night I told her if she went to sleep on her own, the sleep fairy would sprinkle magic fairy dust on her. Miraculously it worked. Five nights out of seven, she sleeps through and I have my life back! For us, waiting until she was ready, and old enough to reason with, worked a treat. It's been tiring at times, but we just went with what we felt she wanted. After all, it's not forever.
Jo from Preston, mum to Faye, four, and Lucy, two

Naps and the older baby

Your older baby will gradually start to require less sleep per 24 hours but, thankfully, it's normal for the reduction to be made in their daytime, rather than night-time sleep. All the same, at least one chunk of daytime sleep will probably still be needed once your baby's reached one, and beyond. The average baby will typically drop from three naps to two at some point before their first birthday, and at some point after that, to a single (but usually substantial) nap in the middle of the day. Your baby will let you know when he's ready to drop a nap, as he just won't seem tired any more at the usual time. The transition period when you are dropping from two naps to one can be a little tricky, and might involve you making adjustments to the rest of his schedule, such as an earlier lunchtime, for a while.

Some older babies begin to resist napping altogether, even if they *are* tired, usually because there are so many more exciting things going on in their lives. You may even find it becomes hard to settle him at all in the daytime, with the potential result that he finally drops off too late in the day and is, therefore, not tired at bedtime. Or he may not nap at all, leaving him overtired, irritable and quite likely to have a disturbed night. If this is a problem for you, persevere in putting him down for regular naps, and don't worry about sticking him in the pushchair or the car in order to encourage sleep, if needs be. Take another look at the tips for encouraging napping on page 91, which may help.

If you're worried your baby is napping too much and it's affecting bedtime settling or night-time sleep for the worse, remember that it's unusual for a baby to sleep more than they need to. As ever, though, naps after 4pm are best avoided if you want your baby to settle down for sleep at a reasonable time of the evening.

Moving your baby out of your bed

If you've been exclusively bedsharing in the early months, you may become ready to turf your little one out now. Maybe you want an uninhibited sex life back. Perhaps you're going back to work and need all the sleep you can get. Or possibly you're expecting another baby and don't think it's going to work to have two in at a time!

It may not be easy overturning the entrenched habits of an older baby who's accustomed to being welcome in your bed, but it's quite possible with a bit of commitment. Generally speaking, the earlier you do this the better, so even if you are still enjoying night-time cuddles, you'd be wise to act now if you think you're likely to tire of the situation in the near future, or there's some practical reason to do so looming.

Making the move

You may find it best to take a gradual approach to moving your baby out of your bed. So, you could try some kind of side-car arrangement for a couple of weeks, perhaps, before putting him in a separate cot, cot-bed or mattress by your bed, and then into his own room. (See the section on page 145 about making the move from cot to bed, and for advice on settling your baby into a new sleeping environment.) You could also take the gradual approach but do it the other way round. In other words, moving him into his own room but going with him, sleeping on a mattress or on a camp bed while he adjusts to being in his own space. If you then need to teach him to settle without you around, a programme of gradual withdrawal (see page 118) could be the next step in the process.

If you're keen to make the move a swift one, however, you can try a 'cold turkey' approach, making the move *and* carrying out sleep training simultaneously. Although this might seem like a lot to take on at once, it can actually work quite well to do both at the same time, rather than tackling both issues in isolation, which will inevitably take twice as long. However, if your baby has been used to lots of attention and your permanent presence at night, it may be kinder to plump for a gentle method like gradual withdrawal or kiss and retreat (see page 118). Whichever route you take, make the first step establishing an independent bedtime and a consistent routine (see page 71), if your baby does not have one of these already.

Even once you've cracked settling him into his own cot or bed and room in the evening, chances are he'll still come to you in the middle of the night for comfort. Or perhaps you are part-time bedsharers and your baby only tends to join you mid-way through the night, anyway. In this case, try 'rapid return' tactics: take him gently by the hand, don't stop to chat, and return him to bed. Stay with him for a little while and offer him soothing words or touch if he needs that to settle (but don't be tempted to get into bed with him or you'll just set up another habit that you need to shed at some point). Don't hang around, though – leave the room as soon as possible. There are no shortcuts to this process and it can require massive amounts of commitment. It's all too easy in the dead of night, when you're exhausted, to turn back the duvet and let your little one hop in. In the end, it's up to you, but you should bear in mind that, ultimately – if getting him out of your bed is what you're aiming for – pain now will mean gain later!

Maggie says: Some parents don't even hear their child come into the bedroom but wake in the morning and find their little one snuggled up in bed with them or lying on the floor beside the bed with a blanket over them. If this happens, you can either manage it by putting a stairgate across their bedroom door to prevent escape, or fix some kind of bell to your own door so you hear them coming in and can return them to their own bed.

What the netmums say

Shifting them out of your bed!

I started co-sleeping with my little one when he was around ten weeks old as I was fed up with not getting a proper night's sleep – it helped him sleep for six hours at a time and I started to feel sane again. We stopped having him in our bed just before his first birthday, as I wanted to stop breastfeeding by then, and we moved him into his own cot, in his own room. We used a controlled crying technique and, as much as I hated it, we were very persistent through about four nights of waking and crying. Since then he's slept right through the night for 10–12 hours at a time.

Samantha from Halesowen, mum to Matthew, one

I co-slept with my daughter from the day she was born. However, by the time she was seven months, I'd had enough of not sleeping properly, enough of not sharing my bed with my partner properly, and enough of breastfeeding all night! We moved her into a cot and prepared for sleep training. But I still had my older two to see to in the evening, so staying in the room until she fell asleep wasn't an option and we went with controlled crying, in the end. I went back to her every five minutes (I couldn't bear to leave her any longer) and comforted her, then left again. By the third night she was asleep within ten minutes of being laid down. She still wakes in the night, but I have my evenings to myself again, and time with my partner as well. I think it's important for babies' development that they learn to settle themselves, and sleep on their own.

Emily from Aylesbury, mum to Aiden, five, William, two, and Jessica, one

Do we have to give up bedsharing?

Don't feel you must give up bedsharing if everyone in the family is genuinely happy with the arrangement – and you're prepared for the possibility of it being a very long-term habit! Some families continue to bedshare for years and even find it works to have more than one child in bed with them. However, it goes without saying that you need to continue to pay close attention to safety guidelines (see page 27) – and have a big enough bed for everyone to fit in safely – if you're going to do this, particularly if one of the parties is a baby under the age of six months.

Equally, you don't have to be beholden to strict bedtimes and consistent evening schedules, if it suits you not to be. Perhaps one or both of you work, and it's the only quality time you get to spend with your little one. Or maybe your baby is a little night owl – and you prefer to have a lie-in in the morning, if that's the fortunate flipside of that situation.

The main thing is to make sure that everyone's getting enough sleep to function well and be healthy in the daytime. If you can honestly say that's happening for you, why worry?

What the netmums say

Happy as we are, thank you

My son has his own bedroom and always goes to bed in his room, but he has the choice of coming in with us if he wakes up in the night and, to be honest, it's about 50/50. Some weeks we wake up every morning to find him asleep between us – along with his blanket, pillow, teddies, water bottle etc! Other weeks he doesn't come in at all – and, to be honest, I then miss it. This works really well for us. We'll carry on as we are unless it becomes a problem.
Vicki from Gillingham, mum to Jake, two

My youngest son is six and still likes to sleep in our bed. He will go to sleep in his own bed if I insist, but rarely sleeps right

through the night in there – he usually turns up in mine anytime between 11pm and 3am. To be honest, I don't find it a problem. My parents think it's disgraceful, but then who wants to be in agreement with their parents about child rearing? My advice is, if it is a priority for *you* (and your partner) to have your child sleeping on his/her own, then be consistent and insist he/she starts there and is returned there every time he/she gets up. It may be exhausting for four to five nights, but it's worth it in the long run. If it isn't a priority, don't bow to pressure from others to move your child out!
Lynsey from Stornoway, mum to Aidan, 18, Beth, 16, Jake, 14, and Cale, six

I started sleeping with my son when he was nine months old. His sleeping had got progressively worse and at that point he was waking up every 45 minutes! Co-sleeping immediately solved the problem and we carried on until he was three, and I was pregnant again. We bought him his own bed and, as we have enough room, we put his bed in our room as I didn't want him to feel pushed out by his new sibling. He's since slept in his own bed with no problems and at four, is still in my bedroom. His baby brother is in bed with me, and has been since he was born. This time round I have had no sleep deprivation as I haven't had to get out of bed in the night. While I appreciate that co-sleeping and family bedrooms are not for everyone, it's been a lifesaver for us. I think if you feel it is a possible solution for your family, you shouldn't be swayed by what other people might think about your sleeping arrangements. In many societies it's the norm!
Shauna from Bristol, mum to Joseph, four, and David, six months

We are a family of co-sleepers, and the children slept with us until they wanted to move into their own beds. I was never sleep deprived. For years we slept like a pile of puppies, happy and peaceful. I don't think we need to teach our children to fall alseep by themselves any more than we need to teach them to breathe. It's been this way for most of human existence.

Sandra from Edinburgh, mum to Joseph, 12, and Joan, nine

I've been co-sleeping with my son from the day he was born. He's now two and, from time to time, I ask him whether he still wants to sleep with Mummy and Daddy (his own bedroom is ready for him to move into whenever he is ready), but he always says 'yes'. He tried it once a couple of months ago and lasted an hour before he said he wanted to come back into Mummy's bed! If he's still co-sleeping at three I *might* start to exert a little more pressure, but he sleeps well with us and we have got used to him being there (me more than my husband, I think!). However, I do sometimes miss just being alone with my husband in bed.

Samantha from Darlington, mum to Jacob, two

Making the move from cot to bed

There's no single 'right time' for transferring your baby from a cot to a bed, but anything from 18 months onwards is usual. You might want to move him if he's growing physically too big to fit in his cot comfortably; or if he's making risky attempts to climb out. Or you might be pregnant again and either need the cot for the new baby, or are just keen to exploit the event to ease the changeover (for more on this, see below).

The move from cot to bed can be a good time to start a sleep-training programme, if you've never done one or if earlier good habits have gone by the wayside. Although it might seem like a lot to take on at once, your little one could see his move as a 'fresh start' and, therefore, be more open to other changes, too.

On the other hand, you may well feel (or your little one might feel) that it's too much to tackle both a move from cot to bed and a changeover in sleep habits at the same time. If this is the case, try looking at it as a two-phase process. Get the move made first, then attempt the sleep training.

Be wary of trying either phase if there's other stuff going on in your baby's life, such as a bout of separation anxiety, a return to work for you, or a new caregiver on the scene – although there's probably no harm in trying a gentler method such as gradual withdrawal at difficult times like these. It's also a good idea to wait if you are currently embroiled in any other major behavioural challenge, such as potty training, otherwise it will be too much for your little one to cope with.

If you're worried about the move from cot to bed generally, you may be reassured to know that for many children it's a very positive step, and that the promotion to a 'big girl' or 'big boy' bed can mark a real turning point in bedtime and sleep habits. Some parents even find the move coincides with the ability to sleep through for the first time, without any extra effort on their part.

Tips for a smooth transition

- A 'toddler' bed which sits close to the ground will provide a safe stepping stone to a full-sized single bed. Cots that convert into small beds are a great idea – although if you have another baby coming, you may need to keep it as a cot anyway, or else buy the new baby a new cot. Some kind of bed guard is also a good idea for safety's sake – at the very least make sure there's a good layer of pillows on the floor in case he should fall out, which is very common while they're getting used to not sleeping behind bars. An alternative is to buy a regular single bed, but initially to use just the mattress on the floor.

- Consider leaving their cot in the room for a while, perhaps even allowing your baby the choice of old cot or new bed. However, it's possible this will prolong a tricky changeover, and you might prefer to just whistle the old cot away altogether, perhaps even storing it out of sight, if possible.

- Try letting your little one have naps in his new bed for a while, before you give night-times a whirl.

- Make a big deal of the move, and what a novelty it all is. Impress upon your little one how 'grown up' he is now (although don't go overboard on this if the move is being driven by a new sibling's imminent arrival, in case it results in resentment). Take him out to buy new bedding or other sleep-related accessories – you could let him try out a new duvet or pillow (it's fine to give your baby a pillow after the age of one) in the cot, first. Equally, though, letting them hold on to some familiar stuff – toys, a pillow case, favourite pyjamas, for example – is a good idea.

- Stick with old rituals and routines, as far as possible.

- Be positive. Offer lots of praise when they do make the move, or at least make a step in the right direction.

- Make sure your child's room is safe in the event of night wanderings: windows should be secure, floors clear of tripping hazards, cords on windows and blinds looped out of reach, and electrical appliances switched off and wires tucked away. If your little one does take to wandering, a stairgate across his door, or at the top of the stairs, is a wise safety precaution (as well as a measure that can help you rectify the situation – see the section on door shutting, above).

When a move equals movement

If your baby has slept well until the change, there's every possibility he won't be affected by it: maybe it won't even occur to him that, just because he *can* get out and about after bedtime now, he *should*. However, you may well find the new-found freedom of a big bed causes you settling or re-settling problems and, in this instance, you'll have to consider one of the sleep-training methods outlined above. Do give him at least a fortnight to settle in to his new bed before going in with sleep-training tactics, however. And meanwhile, try not to lose your cool if he does get out of bed. Just quietly lead him back again, tuck him up, say goodnight, and leave the room – as many times as necessary.

What the netmums say

The move from cot to bed

We're quite lucky with our son, who's always loved his sleep, but we did have a few stumbling blocks when moving him from his cot to a cot-bed at 18 months. The first five nights were heaven: we put him to bed, read him a story, and he went to sleep and stayed there until morning. Then on night six, he realised he could in fact get out of bed! For four long weeks we tried all sorts of tactics to get him to stay there – one night my husband spent three and a half hours continually putting our over-tired, stubborn child back into bed, over and over and over! After about a month we changed tack, and gave him more control of his own bedtime: he could chose whether to have quiet television or a book, then get his own water, turn the telly off or put the books away, and go upstairs and put his own nightlight and monitor on. He could then pick a toy to sleep with, before getting into bed for a final story. It seemed to do the trick – more often than not he was asleep before the end of the book and if he was still awake, he'd be happy to get a kiss and settle himself to sleep once we'd left. I'm not claiming it's perfect *every* night, but we do have a pretty good ratio in our favour and I believe it's because he feels in charge, and not like he's being 'put to bed'.

Vicki from Gillingham, mum to Jake, two

I moved my eldest son into a bed at 17 months as I needed his cot for number two. I did this three to four months before I was due, so he wouldn't feel he'd been pushed out for his new brother. I started with his daytime naps, and put the bed right next to the cot so that if he stirred he would still see the cot. I also kept him in his sleeping bag, so that everything was the same except for the bed. It really wasn't a problem, and after about a week he used the bed all the time. It was literally years before he got out of bed himself – although I did make sure I had the stairgate at the top of the stairs just in case! I also got him to help me move the cot for the new baby, impressing upon him that it was for 'babies' – and that he was a big boy now!

Lucy from Dunblane, mum to Archie, six, and Dugald, four

When I moved my daughter out of her cot, I bought her a Peppa Pig duvet set (Peppa Pig's her favourite) and told her it was a 'big girl's bed'. She was very excited, and the first night went straight to sleep. The second night she realised she could just get up and walk out her bedroom, so I kept taking her back to bed, despite her tantrums. I had to do this for about five nights. But I never gave in and now she goes to bed well, and stays there.
Emma from Bristol, mum to Casey, seven, and Lexie, two

I moved my little girl into her own bed at just over a year, to see if it would improve the situation as she was waking up to eight times a night. We got her a very low-down toddler bed and she loved it – and immediately started to sleep through! In her cot she used to rattle the bars, bang off the sides when she moved and jump up and down, but in her bed she has freedom and lots of room to move. It really did change our lives. She sleeps so well now, and loves bedtime. I plan to move my next one to a big bed even sooner.
Louise from Northampton, mum to Carly, two

The turning point in getting Fae to have a whole night's sleep was putting her in a big girl's bed. We did this when she was 20 months old, as our second baby was on the way. Since then she's slept through almost every night!
Suzanne from St Helens, mum to Fae, three, and Connor, ten months

Siblings and sleep

Life – and sleep solutions – can get even more complicated when you have more than one child in the mix. For instance, how do you establish good sleep habits for a new baby, such as a regular bedtime routine and a consistent napping schedule if you've got the needs of one or more older siblings to attend to? And equally, how do you avoid an older child's existing good sleep habits going by the wayside when a new baby comes along?

Usually when your second (or third, or fourth) child turns up, it's a case of muddling through as best you can and accepting whatever compromises need to be made – with sleep issues being no exception. Fortunately, most parents find that subsequent children often fit uncomplainingly into family life – because they have no choice!

Some sleep solutions for siblings

- Be sensitive if you're moving your little one out of a cot, or your own room or bed, in order to make way for a new baby. It may not be a good idea to insist his 'unwanted' cot is now intended for his sibling, as he's likely to resent giving it up to the new kid on the block. Either make the change with lots of time to spare – at least a month or more, ideally – or forget it and make use of the three- to four-month window after the birth to have the new baby in a crib or Moses basket and give your older one time to get used to things.

- Keep up the older sibling's established bedtime routines as best you can when a younger one arrives. It will help him feel secure in a world that's tipped over, and make for an easier return to normal once the dust has settled. Be sympathetic but stay firm – don't be tempted to cave in because you're over-compensating for a lack of attention elsewhere. Aim to give your older child or children as much of your time as possible (or arrange for another loving caregiver to do so for you) during the day.

- Try not to worry about quietening down your baby for the sake of the older ones. It's good for them to get used to crying as a background noise! Equally, don't insist your older ones tiptoe round the baby or you'll be setting up a very unnatural peace. (It's reasonable, though, to ask them to pipe down a bit if you're trying to settle a younger one.)

- If you're aiming to sleep train a younger child and are worried about disturbing older ones, try doing it during the school holidays when interrupted sleep will matter a bit less. Try selling the process as a bit of an adventure: perhaps your older one will have to camp out in the living room for a while? And involve them in it, too, by explaining what you're doing and enlisting their help – maybe they can help you prepare the new baby's crib, or ask that they be 'very grown-up' about keeping the noise down during bedtime. You might also consider plumping for a gentler method of sleep training, like gradual withdrawal, if you want to avoid your older ones being disturbed by crying. And if you need half an hour's peace to get a younger baby's bedtime routine sorted out and your partner isn't around to entertain the older ones, put them in front of a (calm!) television programme or DVD.

- Don't try sleep training more than one child at a time (unless they are twins, see page 63). If you're tackling a problem in your toddler, leave sorting out your newborn for a while, and vice versa. It'll be too much to cope with in one go.

- Stay philosophical. Life's harder with more than one, it's true. But on the other hand, you've got the benefit of experience – and many parents find they're able to pre-empt a lot of sleep problems in subsequent children having learned so much the first time! You may have a tough time on your hands with a new baby and a wakeful older sibling, with nights even more frequently broken than ever before. But it should be a temporary phase and, if you've already installed good sleep habits in your older child, such as a bedtime routine and the ability to self-settle, they should slot back into place once the novelty of a new baby wears off and the unsettled phase passes. You will probably have to accept and work round the fact that some unhelpful habits are simply unavoidable when you have one or more older siblings to consider: for instance, if you have to go and pick your older child up from school after half past three and that means putting your baby in the car or buggy, which inevitably means them falling asleep later in the day than you'd like!

What the netmums say

Sibling situations

My son was always a good sleeper but my daughter has never slept all night. She had a milk intolerance as a baby, which made her quite poorly, she's not a big eater and didn't start teething until she was one. She goes to bed around 7pm, and usually wakes and cries at least twice before I go to bed. Then she'll normally wake twice during the night and need milk to get her back to sleep – I know this is for comfort rather than hunger as she's slept all the way through in the past, when we've let her into our bed. I think I'll have to accept it and hope she grows

out of it. Unfortunately, it disturbs her brother as they share a room.
Sarah from New Malden, mum to Josh, six, and Libby, one

Mine have all slept very differently. Elana was a champion sleeper by six months, going down at 7.30pm and waking up at 9am. Gabriel was awake every two hours at least through the night until he was 18 months old. Isaac sleeps from 8.30pm through to 6amish, and has done from about six weeks. Neither of the older two changed their patterns at all when a younger sibling came along, though. The only difference is when the routine changes for some reason; with three I find it harder to get back into the swing of things.
Charlotte from Elgin, mum to Elana, six, Gabriel, three, and Isaac, nine months

We had lots of problems with our oldest but our second baby was a different child from the start. We were also different parents. He had a bedtime routine from day one and it really seemed to work. His sleep started to stretch out and by eight months he would sleep from 7pm through to 5am with only a dream feed at 10pm as we went to bed.
Suzanne from St Helens, mum to Fae, three, and Connor, ten months

We moved Holly into her new room two months before Jake was born. She's always been a good sleeper and settled into the room well. But since the birth, she's mucked about every single night: we put her to bed at 7.45pm and she'll still be awake gone 9pm, shouting, crying, screaming and messing up her room. She thinks Jake is in bed, she doesn't know we take him downstairs, so I hate to think how she'd react if she discovered that. We're trying to get the baby to settle in his cot in the evenings now, but with all Holly's shouting and screaming she's keeping him awake.

Lucy from Basildon, mum to Holly, two, and Jake, four months

My eldest daughter had no problems sleeping through and being on her own upstairs. But since the youngest has been born, it's a struggle to keep her out of my room and bed. She comes in at different times, with different problems – mainly it's that she's had a nightmare or a bad dream. I thought at first she felt left out so I let her stay in my bed at weekends but kept her in her own bed during the week so her sleep was undisturbed for school. Sometimes she looks so tired and I know she's been lying in bed awake for ages. And sometimes, she comes in so many times I just let her get in!

Vicki from Stevenage, mum to Caitlin, six, and Freya, nine months

Night-time fears

Although most commonly suffered by children of two or more, night-time fears – a very normal part of development – can become an issue from 18 months onwards. With their growing minds and imaginations, toddlers of this age start to become aware of scary stuff, yet still struggle with the difference between reality and fantasy, and, unsurprisingly, the belief that monsters lurk under their bed, or that the shadows on their walls are alive, can affect settling or sleeping for the worse.

Be patient and sympathetic if your child is suffering from night-time fears. Stay with him and offer comfort if he needs it to settle. Be wary of using it to set up new unhelpful habits, or reinstate any old ones, though – allowing him into your bed when he's scared, for example (if that's something you don't normally do) or offering a bottle of milk in the middle of the night, when you've long before cracked a night-time feeding problem. Be kind, but firm. Thankfully phases of night-time fears are always temporary and eventually pass.

> **Maggie says:** It's important to understand and acknowledge a child's night-time fears, and to allow them their feelings. What seem to us trivial can be very real and very upsetting to them, and they need to be comforted and reassured. However, you still need to maintain your usual boundaries, as consistency helps your child to feel secure and safe.

Easing night-time fears in your little one

- Keep an eye on what he's watching or reading. Something in a particular book or programme may have triggered a fear, in which case, aim to identify it and remove it.
- Make bedtime (and the hour or so before it) a calm, relaxing experience, and keep up all your old rituals: it will help your child feel secure when bedtime comes round.
- Allow him a nightlight, if the dark is bothering him, or keep his door open and the landing light on.
- Read him gentle story books last thing, with appropriate plotlines about young characters who've experienced night-time fears, such as *Cassie and the Kiss Soldier* by Marion Rose and Vanessa Cabban, *"I'm Not Scared!"* by Jonathan Allen, *Can't You Sleep, Little Bear?* by Martin Waddell, or *Tell Me Something Happy Before I Go to Sleep* by Joyce Dunbar and Debi Gliori.

- Don't dismiss your child's fears. If he is old enough to have a conversation with you, talk about it and give lots of reassurance that he has nothing to worry about. Asking an older toddler to draw pictures of, or act out, what's scaring them in the daytime can be a good way of dealing with it.
- Help him to relax just before going to bed with the aid of massage, a soothing story or a music tape, or some simple deep-breathing exercises.

Louise says: Don't blame yourself if your child is going through a frightened phase, or fret too much about why it's happening. It's really not that unusual and is rarely a sign that your child is overtly worried about anything.

Night terrors

Occasionally, a child under two may suffer from what's known as night terrors, or confusional arousal, although they are more common in older children. Night terrors occur during dream sleep (see page 17), when a child partially wakes and appears terrified, perhaps screaming or flailing their limbs around, for anything up to thirty minutes. Witnessing night terrors can be horribly scary for parents and, as the child is still asleep, it's impossible to soothe them.

It's best not to attempt to wake a child in the middle of a night terror, but to stay with them and offer lots of physical comfort. They may be wide awake after the night terror ends, in which case, you may need to help them get off to sleep again. The good news is that the child isn't aware of what's happening during a night terror and won't remember it. They are always outgrown in time, but if your baby suffers from recurrent night terrors, chat to your GP or health visitor. They may recommend a treatment which involves waking your little one about 15 minutes before the night terror usually kicks in, in an attempt to break the pattern, or may even suggest medication.

Louise says: Seeing your child experience a night terror can be very distressing. Toddlers will not only cry out but may run around appearing crazed, and also will often reject any sort of physical comforting. Try not to intervene at all when it's happening and, once it's over, just ensure they are safely back in bed.

7 Special problems . . . and some specific solutions

More than just a habit?

Most sleep problems are caused by perfectly ordinary behavioural issues and can be tackled with the various strategies outlined so far. However, sometimes a very specific cause is at play, such as illness, and it's important to be alert to that possibility. In most cases, tackling this root problem will solve the sleeping issue: or at least, it will get you to a point where your baby is healthy enough for you to tackle it in the normal way.

Teething

Not all babies experience problems sleeping as a result of teething, which can occur at any time but typically begins after six months. However, there is no doubt that, for some, it causes misery and discomfort that disturbs their nights.

Other symptoms that indicate teething are red, hot cheeks, excessive dribbling, a loss of appetite (or even a refusal to feed), an increased tendency to chew things and general irritability. There's also anecdotal (rather than medical) evidence linking teething with loose stools (thought to be caused by the excess saliva passing through the tummy) and nappy rash (again, a result of excess saliva, which makes the stools acidic). In any case, it's important to bear in mind that any of these symptoms could also be a sign that your child has an illness which needs medical attention. If in any doubt, check with your GP, or give NHS Direct a call.

Fortunately teething discomfort should only ever cause two to three nights of disruption and, with any luck, it won't affect any existing good sleep habits. If it does, your best bet is to get things back on track as soon as possible once the phase is over. Meanwhile, if teething discomfort strikes at night, there are a number of things you can try to offer your baby to give her some relief for just long enough to settle her again.

Sleep solutions for teething babies

- Rub a little teething gel on your baby's gums. These numb the pain for around 20 minutes.
- Offer the appropriate dose of an infant paracetamol or ibuprofen.
- Try homeopathic teething powders, which some mums report to be effective.
- While a good idea in the daytime, teething rings might be best avoided at night, as they could be a distraction that will keep your baby awake. Never give food or anything else which might be a choking hazard while she's lying down.
- Help to prevent soreness around the mouth during times of

teething, by wiping a little Vaseline around her mouth at bedtime.

- Offering the breast or bottle may soothe teething discomfort (although sometimes feeding can make the discomfort worse) but only if your baby is still feeding at night, anyway. Don't be tempted to do so if you've managed to kick a night-time feeding habit, as you could very quickly be back to square one. You should probably resist picking her up for a cuddle, too, or you might just be setting up a whole new unhelpful sleep association. Offer a bottle of water and a stroke or pat, instead.

- If teething issues have disrupted existing good habits, aim to get life back to normal as soon as possible once the phase is over. If you've already beaten a night-waking habit and you find she has started waking again, you may be dismayed by the prospect of having to sleep train again – however, you should find that, once cracked for a first time, it is more quickly and easily achieved on subsequent attempts.

- Don't attempt to *start* any kind of sleep-training programme if you know your baby is experiencing discomfort because of teething problems. Wait for the phase to pass first.

Nappy rash

A sore bottom could potentially wake your little one at night, or prevent her from settling in the evening. Nappy rash is a very common irritation, usually caused by prolonged contact with urine or poo but, occasionally and more seriously, is caused by a fungal infection (for which she may need treatment, so check with your health visitor or GP if it seems severe or doesn't clear up after a few days).

If you know your baby is suffering from a bout of nappy rash and you suspect it's the cause of her sleep disturbance, a quick wipe with warm water and cotton wool, a fresh nappy and a dab of medicated nappy cream should make her comfortable enough to settle again. Do so quickly, quietly and without turning the lights on, though, and, with any luck, she'll be back to sleep again very soon.

Colds and coughs

Babies often fall prey to minor illnesses like coughs and colds, because their immune systems are immature, and symptoms such as a blocked nose, high temperature, cough and sore throat can of course lead to disturbed nights.

As a general rule it's a good idea to stick with a bedtime routine when your child's poorly, but a bad idea to start a sleep-training programme. If you're already in the middle of sleep training when your child falls ill, you may need to call a halt for a while, and start again when the illness is over. A lot will depend on how poorly she is and what strategy you're taking. (It might be ok to carry on with a gentle method, such as gradual withdrawal, but probably won't be a good idea to carry on with controlled crying, for example.) Follow your instincts and do what seems right but, whatever you do, try to avoid letting your baby's illness trigger (or re-instate) any habits you could do without, such as bringing her into bed with you. If she's unhappy and needs your company, go to her. And aim to get back into the swing of any established routines and good habits as promptly as possible: you may well find the disruption is nothing more than a temporary blip.

Do consult your GP if your little one has cold symptoms that hang around for a week or more, if she is wheezing or seems to have trouble breathing, or her temperature goes above 38 degrees centigrade.

Louise says: Babies get many colds and other minor illnesses in their first year of life. If you're sleep training, it's very likely to be disturbed at these times – you'll need to gauge for yourself whether to abandon it altogether or whether to make allowances and go easy.

Dr David says: It's difficult to give advice on sleep training when a baby is unwell. I wouldn't advise starting a sleep-training programme unless your baby's in the best of health, and if you happen to be in the middle of one when your baby falls ill, you have to do the right thing and go with what your baby, and you, can cope with, rather than be too rigid. What is a good idea is taking up where you left off as soon as possible once your baby is well again.

Tips for tackling cold symptoms at night

- Keeping the air in the room moist. Room humidifiers are available to buy, but are expensive – putting a bowl of water by the radiator or just draping some wet laundry over it will serve the same purpose.
- Clearing nasal congestion, either by using a nasal aspirator or emptying an inhalant decongestion capsule into a bowl of water and putting it close to the cot or bed (don't offer on a hanky or tissue for babies under six months, as they are too strong). Baby vapour rubs may be a help to babies of six months or more, applied to their back and chest, and – over a layer of Vaseline – just under the nose. For babies under three months, saline nasal drops may be prescribed by a GP. Raising the top half of your baby's mattress by

putting cushions or books under it at the head end can also help to relieve congestion.

- In the case of a fever, giving a dose of an appropriate infant antipyretic (a drug that reduces temperature), such as Calpol. Make sure any medication you give is appropriate for your baby's age, and you are giving the correct dosage. Cough and cold medications are not usually suitable for young babies and have little benefit. If in any doubt, ask your health visitor, pharmacist or GP first. As a general rule, keep a close eye on feverishness, particularly if accompanied by vomiting, and seek medical advice if you're concerned.

- Giving her lots of fluids. Try to avoid offering milk at night, though, if this is a habit you have already broken – give water, instead, and offer plenty of extra milk feeds in the day if she wants them.

- Keep an eye on her temperature. She shouldn't be any hotter or colder than usual, so check her room thermometer and her bedding and bedclothes, and alter if necessary.

- Try to accept that an illness will mean disturbed nights for a while and give your baby as much comfort as possible in the meantime.

Ear infections

Ear infections are also a common minor illness in babies, caused as a result of a build-up of mucus in the middle ear – often after a cold. They can lead to painful earache, which tends to get worse when lying down so, not surprisingly, they can make for an uncomfortable and disrupted night for your baby. Some babies can end up getting ear infections repeatedly, which can cause major disruption to good sleep habits – and are especially frustrating if they start cropping up once you've succeeded in getting your little one to sleep through the night.

Giving your baby the appropriate dose of infant paracetamol or ibuprofen should ease the pain long enough to allow her to settle, if she's disturbed by the pain of an ear infection.

In most cases ear infections will clear up on their own, but if your baby has one that persists beyond a few days, see your GP as antibiotics may be required.

Gastro-oesophageal reflux

This common problem (which you may also hear referred to as reflux, acid reflux, silent reflux or gastro-oesophageal reflux disorder or GORD) occurs when the acidic contents of the stomach are regurgitated back into the oesophagus or throat, causing pain and discomfort, laboured or fast breathing, or vomiting. As it most commonly strikes after a feed and is exacerbated when your baby is lying down flat, it's very likely to cause problems with settling and sleeping. In some cases, reflux symptoms occur without the vomiting, and this is when it's usually known as silent reflux.

Putting your baby to sleep on a cot mattress that's been raised to a 30 degree angle with pillows placed underneath, at your baby's head end, may give her some relief. You can also buy special wedges and 'sleep positioners' designed to help keep a baby at this slightly raised angle – check with your health visitor or doctor before using anything like this, though, and bear in mind the importance of the back-to-sleep safety guidelines (see page 22). Allowing your baby at least half an hour after her last feed before putting her down for the night could help, and it's also a good idea to keep her as upright as possible during the feed, and for a while afterwards. And there are now special formula milks available on the market – your health visitor or GP can advise you. They may also prescribe medication, such as Gaviscon Infant, which works by thickening the contents of the stomach.

Reflux is caused because the valve action of the lower oesophageal sphincter – the muscular ring at the lower end of the oesophagus – is not yet developed, and babies usually grow out of symptoms at some point between six and 18 months. It can be exacerbated by an allergy or intolerance (see below), and can also cause sleep apnoea so it's worth ruling these out with your GP if you suspect it. A useful source of further information and support is included in the back of the book.

Allergies and eczema

Up to 20 per cent of babies suffer from atopic eczema (also known as dermatitis), a chronic, inflammatory condition that can leave the skin red, cracked, itchy and dry and, unsurprisingly, can lead to miserable, disturbed nights, which for many parents and little ones are the worst aspect of this condition. An allergy to cows' milk (see below) is also common in babies with eczema as the two are linked.

If your baby is affected, your health visitor and GP can help you find ways to control the symptoms and ease the misery. Treatments include emollient creams and bath oils, which can help to moisturise and soothe the skin and, in severe cases, medication in the form of steroids. For short-term relief from night-time itching, your GP may prescribe Piriton, an antihistamine that also has a sedative effect, or recommend the use of 'wet wraps'. Other ways to manage the condition and avoid potential triggers include avoiding the use of normal soaps or lotions, limiting baths, which can be drying, using non-biological detergents for your laundry, and keeping your home dust free.

Moisturising your baby at bedtime, dressing her in pure cotton sleepsuits at night, and using pure cotton bedding for her may also help. If itching is a problem, keep her nails short to help avoid scratching, which could cause an infection. If she'll keep them on, a pair of cotton scratch mitts or socks over her hands can help prevent this, too, and you can also buy specialist sleep suits with integral mitts.

Serious sleep disturbances can also be caused by cows' milk allergy (CMA) and lactose intolerance. They are different problems: cows' milk allergy is a reaction by the immune system to the proteins in milk, which can cause eczema symptoms, and wheezing or coughing, as well as gastrointestinal problems like vomiting, cramps and diarrhoea; lactose intolerance – which is much more rare – occurs when a baby has difficulty digesting milk sugar and symptoms include abdominal pain and discomfort, excess wind and diarrhoea.

Any problems with sleeping are likely to be resolved once you've tackled the allergy or intolerance, so it's vital to seek help from your health visitor or GP if you suspect either of these problems. If diagnosed, your child is likely to be prescribed a special hypoallergenic formula milk or, if you're breastfeeding, you'll be advised on ways to avoid potential trigger foods in your own diet. In any case, it's essential to check with a doctor before making any changes to your baby's diet (or yours).

Maggie says: Generally speaking, if you can get the eczema or allergy under control, you'll find the sleep problem disappears anyway. If not – and as long as you are sure the symptoms are under control and they are no longer suffering – there's no reason why you can't sleep train a child with one of these conditions.

Sleep apnoea

Apnoea is the medical term used to describe temporary pauses in breathing, and it's a condition that can cause babies (as well as older children and adults) to wake at night. There are three sorts of apnoea:

obstructive sleep apnoea (OSA), which is caused by a blockage – usually excess tissue in the back of the throat – and tends to affect adults and older children; central sleep apnoea, caused by a neurological dysfunction and this is the sort that is most likely to affect young babies; and mixed apnoea, which is a very rare combination of both.

Although apnoea is rarely life threatening in babies, it's important to seek medical advice if you're concerned that your baby's affected. As well as repeated pauses in breathing during sleep that are longer than 15–20 seconds (bearing in mind that short pauses are quite normal, especially in very young babies – see page 36), you may notice your little one gasping as she takes a breath at the end of a pause. In the case of obstructive sleep apnoea, your baby may be breathing noisily or dribbling a lot, or snoring or making wheezing noises as she sleeps. Excessive tiredness or crabbiness during the day, where there's no other explanation, could also be a sign that apnoea is affecting a child's night-time sleep.

Premmie babies are commonly affected by apnoea – it's then known as apnoea of prematurity – as they have underdeveloped respiratory systems. However, any risks will have usually passed by the time your baby has reached term and been discharged from hospital.

Although research has been carried out to try and establish an association between apnoea and cot death, no significant evidence has been found to suggest one. Sometimes, apnoea monitors (see page 11) are provided to parents who've previously suffered the loss of a child to cot death for peace of mind. (As they are prone to 'false alarms', however, they can cause more anxiety than they ease.)

Special needs

Once in a while, sleep problems that don't seem to respond to the obvious measures and go on long past infancy may turn out to be a factor in a special need such as autism, dyspraxia, or attention deficit hyperactivity disorder (ADHD), all of which have been known to cause sleep or settling problems in children. Although these conditions tend to be diagnosed later in childhood, it's worth being alert to the possibility in your toddler, if sleep problems persist and no other explanation seems to fit the bill. Chat to your health visitor or GP about it, if you have any concerns.

Maggie says: Sometimes, when a parent has done everything to solve a long-term sleep problem and nothing has worked, despite their best efforts, it transpires that the problem is more deep-seated and lies within the child's special needs. Of course, there may well be other clues as well, in their general behaviour. It's a possibility to bear in mind.

What the netmums say

Medical reasons for sleep problems

We battled to get our daughter to sleep in the evening (starting from 7pm and ending anytime between 8pm and 11pm). Once asleep she'd wake for feeds, and then take forever to settle down again. Eventually it turned out she had reflux (hence the constant difficulty in settling her after feeding) so she's been on Gaviscon Infant and has slept with her cot tilted ever since. So long as I sit her upright for ten minutes after a feed so she can burp and have a quick vom, she's happy to go to sleep.

Julie from London, mum to Edith, five months

At around eight months old, our son started developing a digestive illness which gave him a lot of pain. He'd wake up

all hours of the night and his appetite was up and down. Unfortunately, it wasn't identified or treated by the many different doctors we saw and it got worse, culminating in him needing emergency surgery at 13 months, followed by a month's stay in hospital. During this time, I decided to stop breastfeeding. It was only while in hospital that he started sleeping through the night in a cot of his own, and back home, he continued to do so. We don't know why, but we always wanted it to be something he got to when *he* was ready, rather than something that we tried to push him towards. When I look back on those months when we barely got any sleep, I don't know how we managed to get through it, but we did. It was hard, but the stress of trying to make sure he slept through the night would have made things a lot worse. I knew he was waking for a reason and I didn't want to ignore those reasons for our own convenience.
Tammy from Walthamstow, mum to Jake, one

Things were going really well with our youngest. Then he had a bad month with teething, croup, pneumonia and gastroenteritis all in the space of three weeks! Sleep went out of the window as he got used to being nursed and cuddled. He's now recovered but has reverted to waking every two hours and not being able to settle to sleep on his own. Our resilience is wearing thin.
Suzanne from St Helens, mum to Fae, three, and Connor, ten months

My youngest, Charlie, was never a great sleeper. Then, at ten months he caught chicken pox and went from sleeping from 7pm to 5am, with one feed at midnight, to waking every two hours. I was breastfeeding him every two hours while he was ill, which I was ok with, but as the weeks went by I guess it became a habit, for both of us. I became exhausted and couldn't think straight to even try to tackle it. Eventually, I tried a technique that I'd heard of and sort of adapted it. When Charlie cried I went into his room, kept the room dark, avoided eye contact but just placed my hand on him to reassure him. I'd do a quick check if he was wet or too hot or cold, then keep my hand still. At first, he cried out with frustration that I wasn't picking him up. I didn't think I'd be able to carry on but I kept calm (singing nursery rhymes in my head, thinking of lazy days on the beach) and stayed positive that it would work. It did. He cried for about 15 minutes the first night, then stopped only to start again about half an hour later. The first three nights were the worst. After that he probably woke twice a night. Then eventually, I'd hear him stir, cry out and then settle himself. It wasn't easy, and took about three weeks to crack it, but now he goes to bed at 7pm every night and sleeps through till 6.30–7am. He's a happy, active toddler and I've got the energy (most of the time) to keep up with him.

Michelle from Shrewsbury, mum to Tom, four, and Charlie, one

My son was a brilliant sleeper until he reached about four months and then was waking about eight times a night. When we started weaning at six months, the night wakings increased to about every 45 minutes. I was encouraged by everyone to leave him to cry but something told me there was more to it than just him not sleeping, so I persevered with rocking him before putting him down and then patting his bottom until he was out. We finally found out he had an extensive list of allergies and had been in pain for the last four months. Once all the problem foods were removed from his

diet, I just had to feed him, put him in his cot, and pat his bottom to sleep. After a couple of weeks of this I would only pat for a minute, then leave the room. Slowly the night wakings got less and less until the night before his first birthday he slept through the night! He now goes down to sleep on his own after his bedtime feed. Everyone told me that the only way he would ever learn was to leave him to cry but I'm glad I stuck to my guns and let him do it when he was ready.
Bronwen from Bristol, mum to Oscar, one

My daughter has reflux. She's been on Gaviscon Infant since birth but this wasn't enough for her. I had to try to cope with her screaming for up to eight hours at a time every day and night while trying to tell our GP that there was something seriously wrong with her! He thought it was colic and that she would grow out of it. Eventually we took matters into our own hands and went to a private doctor. He diagnosed reflux and prescribed medication, which has changed her life, and ours. Without it I think we would all have gone mad!
Michelle from Strathaven, mum to Abby, one

Alternative approaches

Some parents have found they can ease sleep or settling problems with the help of 'alternative' approaches. While there isn't much medical evidence that these will *definitely* help your baby sleep better, some people swear by them . . . and you might feel that anything's worth a try!

Cranial osteopathy / craniosacral therapy

Cranial osteopathy involves the gentle manipulation of the skull, to relieve pressure and tension in the skull caused during birth, which can cause – among other problems – a baby's nervous system to be oversensitive, and hence they are easily woken. It's also said to relieve related problems, such as colic, feeding and settling difficulties (see page 56), and nasal congestion. If you want to give it a try, be sure to seek out a registered practitioner (and be prepared to pay, as you won't get cranial osteopathy on the NHS). For more information, contact the Sutherland Society (details for this and all other organisations mentioned here are in the back of the book).

Craniosacral therapy is also based on the theory that compression during birth can cause babies lasting problems, although the technique is different. Find out more from the Craniosacral Therapy Association of the UK.

Homeopathy

This alternative system of medicine is based on treatment with highly diluted substances that trigger the body's natural system of healing. Homeopathic remedies said to promote calm and aid sleep are available from health food shops and large chemists, but your best bet is to seek professional help. It's worth asking your GP about homeopathy as, unlike some forms of alternative medicine, this is sometimes covered by the NHS. Alternatively, you can find a registered private homeopath. For more information, contact the British Homeopathic Society.

Aromatherapy and massage

This treatment makes use of natural plant extracts, known as essential oils, and is said to offer healing for a variety of ills. For baby sleep problems, it's usually administered in the form of massage oil, although it can also be used by adding essential oils to a bowl of water to make a room fragrant, or in a bath. On its own, baby massage can help to relax and calm a baby, and can be an enjoyable part of a regular bedtime routine for both of you. As with all other alternative treatments, be sure to find a registered practitioner. Find out more at the Aromatherapy Council, and from the International Association of Infant Massage. (You can also find out about baby massage classes available near you on the local boards on Netmums.)

Reflexology

Reflexologists use a special compression technique on the feet, in order to detect imbalances in the body and release congestions that stop it working efficiently. In babies, these techniques are said to have a number of benefits, including the easing of colic and sleep problems. There are also courses available offering you the chance to learn how to treat your baby with reflexology. For more information and a list of qualified practitioners, contact the Association of Reflexologists.

Diet

If your baby's older than six months and fully weaned, it could aid her sleep to pay attention to what she's eating in the hours before bedtime, as some foods have natural sedative effects (and others, the opposite!).

- Anything containing the amino acid tryptophan is a good bet, as it aids the production of melatonin, the sleep hormone. These include poultry (especially turkey), bananas, dairy products, green leafy vegetables, kidney beans, tuna, seeds, oats, eggs and soya products. Nuts are another good source of tryptophan but if there's a history of allergies in your baby's immediate family, it's currently recommended that you wait three years before offering her peanuts. And whole nuts shouldn't be offered before the age of one, as they're a choking hazard. (It's always a good idea, however, to offer all new foods to your baby one at a time, allowing a day or two in between, just in case of an allergic reaction.) To really boost the effect of tryptophan, you should serve some carbohydrates such as pasta, bread, or rice, alongside it as these produce the hormone insulin, which will help the tryptophan reach the brain and do its job.

- The mineral calcium is also said to have a calming effect, which is why – along with the tryptophan effect (see above) – warm milk, or breastmilk or formula for the under ones, makes the perfect bedtime drink. Good sources of calcium other than milk include: cheese and yoghurt, white bread, dried fruits, leafy green veg such as broccoli, oranges, pulses and canned sardines. Another mineral, magnesium, is known to be a muscle relaxant – bananas are a great source.

- Include some protein in your baby's last meal of the day, as these will help fill her up – good sources are meat, fish, beans and pulses, dairy produce, eggs, nuts and soya.

- The timing of your baby's evening meal is relevant, too. It's a good idea to try and make sure your baby's main meal is at lunchtime, with a lighter meal given for tea. In any case, try to allow at least an hour between teatime and bedtime, so she has plenty of time to digest it.

- Keep sugary foods to a minimum before bedtime, as sugar stimulates the nervous system. It probably goes without saying that caffeine should be avoided (as well as being found in coffee and tea, it's a common ingredient in many fizzy drinks and chocolate). And some additives are linked to hyperactivity in children: as a very general rule, avoid anything with either red, yellow or blue food colouring in it.

What the netmums say

Alternative therapies

Abigail had terrible sleep problems. She woke on average every two to three hours a night until she was around 19 months old. I'd tried everything and finally, as a last resort, I took her to see a cranial osteopath. The following night she slept for six hours and by the end of the week was sleeping for up to eight hours a night. She had several treatments and I was told her sleep problem was caused by her traumatic birth. She's been a good sleeper ever since – and I now take both her and her brother once or twice a year for treatment, which always seems to improve their levels of contentment.

Lisa from Caterham, mum to Abigail, five, and William, one

Sometimes I use aromatherapy to help my boys relax and have a good night's sleep (although admittedly it doesn't *always* work). I put lavender on a muslin near my boys' bed, or chamomile and lavender in their bathwater. I also use lemon and eucalyptus in an oil burner when they have a cold.

Irma from Oldham, mum to Damir, two, and Aydin, eight months

Medication

Although there are a number of different sorts of medication available both on prescription and over-the-counter that can aid sleep, they are not generally to be recommended for healthy babies – there may be side effects and, in any case, it's unlikely to provide an effective long-term solution. You'll only achieve that if you tackle the problem head-on. Your doctor may consider prescribing a short-term course of medication, if you're really at the end of your tether, in order to give you a short break and with a view to breaking the cycle.

Never give your baby any kind of over-the-counter medication in the hope it will help aid sleep, without first seeking advice from your GP, health visitor, or pharmacist.

Dr David says: Although there are a number of medications on the market, most doctors would be reluctant to prescribe them for healthy babies except perhaps as a last resort, and as a temporary measure. Almost all sleep problems – unless your baby has a diagnosed medical problem, or special need of some kind – are best tackled with a careful look at your lifestyle and habits and, if necessary, a committed programme of sleep training.

Getting professional help

If your own efforts to solve a sleep problem have failed, you've ruled out any medical causes, and you can't go on much longer but aren't sure what to do next, do consider seeking some professional help. Have a chat to your GP or health visitor first, as they may be able to refer you to an NHS-run sleep clinic if there's one in your area. If not, and finances will stretch to it, you could look into seeking help from a private sleep clinic (some are listed in the back of the book). If things are really bad, it could be an investment worth making.

What the netmums say

Seeking professional help

My health visitor referred us to a sleep therapist because at 13 months, my daughter was not sleeping through the night. The sleep therapist worked through a few different methods with me to 'train' Jessica to sleep at night. The one that worked for us was a method of controlled crying (I understand it isn't for everyone) but I had to use a good routine to prepare her for the bedtime and the controlled crying, which I did by using a lavender-scented bedtime bath wash, and making sure she had a warm drink before bed. By the end of week one, she was able to sleep all night from 7.30pm right through until 8am the following morning. So the help and reassurance I got from the sleep therapist made a huge difference. I doubt I'd have had the confidence to try controlled crying without it.

Anmarie from Bolton, mum to Jessica, one

After seven months of virtually no sleep and feeling like I couldn't take any more, I took Grace to a private sleep clinic. With their help I started a 'dummy detox', and a programme of controlled crying. I must say it's been hard, but it's working, as I've had more sleep in this past week than in the past seven months put together. I don't want to go back to what it was like before, and I'd advise anyone who's desperate to consider getting professional help.

Kareen from Dalkeith, mum to Grace, nine months

Appendix: Sources of help and further information

Safe sleep advice

FSID: www.fsid.org.uk

Colic and crying

Cry-sis
Helpline: 08451 228 669
www.cry-sis.org.uk

Postnatal depression

www.overcomingpnd.com
www.pni.org.uk

Premature birth

Bliss: www.bliss.org.uk

24 hour medical advice

NHS DIRECT: 0845 4647
www.nhsdirect.nhs.uk
NHS24 (for Scotland): 08454 242424
www.nhs24.com

Multiples

Tamba: www.tamba.org.uk
Twins UK: www.twinsuk.co.uk
Multiple Births Foundation: www.multiplebirths.org.uk
More Than One: www.morethan1.org.uk

Safe bedsharing advice

Unicef: www.babyfriendly.org.uk/pdfs/sharingbedleaflet/pdf
National Childbirth Trust: www.nctpregnancyandbabycare.com

Reflux

www.babyreflux.co.uk

Eczema

National Eczema Society
Helpline: 0800 089 1122
www.eczema.org

Alternative treatments

Sutherland Society: www.cranial.org.uk

Craniosacral Therapy Association of the UK: www.craniosacral.co.uk
British Homeopathic Society: www.britishhomeopathic.org
Aromatherapy Council: www.aromatherapycouncil.co.uk
International Association of Infant Massage UK: www.iaim.org.uk
Association of Reflexologists: www.aor.org.uk

Private sleep clinics

Millpond: www.mill-pond.co.uk
Naturally Nurturing: www.naturallynurturing.co.uk
Andrea Grace: www.andreagrace.co.uk

Further reading

What Every Parent Needs to Know by Margot Sunderland (Dorling Kindersley, 2007)
The Continuum Concept by Jean Liedloff (Penguin, 1986)
Three in a Bed by Deborah Jackson (Bloomsbury, 2003)
The Complete Sleep Guide for Contented Babies and Toddlers by Gina Ford (Vermillion, 2003)
The Baby Whisperer Solves All Your Problems by Tracy Hogg with Melinda Blau (Vermillion, 2005)
Solve Your Child's Sleep Problems by Dr Richard Ferber (Dorling Kindersley, 2006)
New Toddler Taming by Christopher Green (Vermillion, 2001)
Teach Your Child to Sleep by Millpond Sleep Clinic (Hamlyn, 2005)
The No-Cry Sleep Solution by Elizabeth Pantley (McGraw-Hill, 2002)
Solving Children's Sleep Problems by Lyn Quine (Beckett-Karlson, 1997)
The Baby Sleep Bible by Jo Wiltshire (Crimson, 2009)

Index

More **netmums** *titles from Headline*

HOW TO BE A HAPPY MUM

with Siobhan Freegard

Stop trying to be the perfect mum. Learn how to be a happy mum.

Having young children is supposed to be the happiest time of your life. But it's not always easy to make the most of the joys of motherhood. You're tired. The kids are playing up. The fridge is empty. The house is a state. And you can't remember when you last had some time to yourself. But while there's no shortage of advice on how to care for babies and children, who is looking after you?

How to Be a Happy Mum identifies the top ten stresses mothers have to cope with and offers sound advice on how to overcome them – from feelings of loneliness, to quieting tantruming toddlers, to managing a hectic home. The advice comes from hand-selected experts and, most importantly, from other mothers who have been there, done it and lived to tell the tale: the members of **netmums** the UK's fastest-growing online parenting community.

How to Be a Happy Mum tells you how to care for yourself – the person most likely to be forgotten when raising a family. After all, how can you hope to raise happy children if you haven't discovered how to be a happy mum?

NON-FICTION/PARENTING 978 0 7553 1606 9

More netmums *titles from Headline*

TODDLING TO TEN

with Hollie Smith

Children bring great joy. But they also bring problems. Lots of them.

What do you do when your toddler throws a tantrum for no obvious reason? How do you cope when the only thing they'll eat is Yorkshire pudding and bananas? And how exactly do you stop them from knocking six bells out of their long-suffering sibling?

Life with children is full of challenges, but short on solutions. Fortunately, the members of netmums the UK's fastest-growing online parenting community, have the answers.

Toddling to Ten looks at the most common parenting problems – from ditching the dummy to beating bullying – and offers hundreds of tips alongside the personal stories of the netmums members themselves, as well as solid advice from a hand-selected panel of experts.

Toddling to Ten is full of real advice, for real mums, with real children.

FREE P&P AND UK DELIVERY
(Overseas and Ireland £3.50 per book)

To order, simply call 01235 400 414
visit our website: www.headline.co.uk
or email orders@bookpoint.co.uk

Prices and availability are subject to change without notice.

NON-FICTION/PARENTING 978 0 7553 1607 6

www.netmums.com

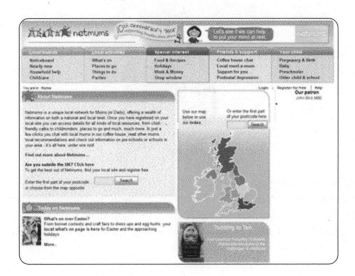

netmums is a dedicated website for families.

Ages-and-stages information about babies, toddlers and older children is offered alongside forums to bring you together with mums from all over the country to share experiences and advice, or just pass the time of day.

There is lots of local information about where to go and what to do with babies and children in your area including groups, classes, activities and family events. Meet other local mums through the meet-a-mum board and find out about groups nearby that meet regularly.

Parent Supporters are on hand to offer online advice and support on any aspect of family life that is causing you worry.

Log onto www.netmums.com and visit your local site.